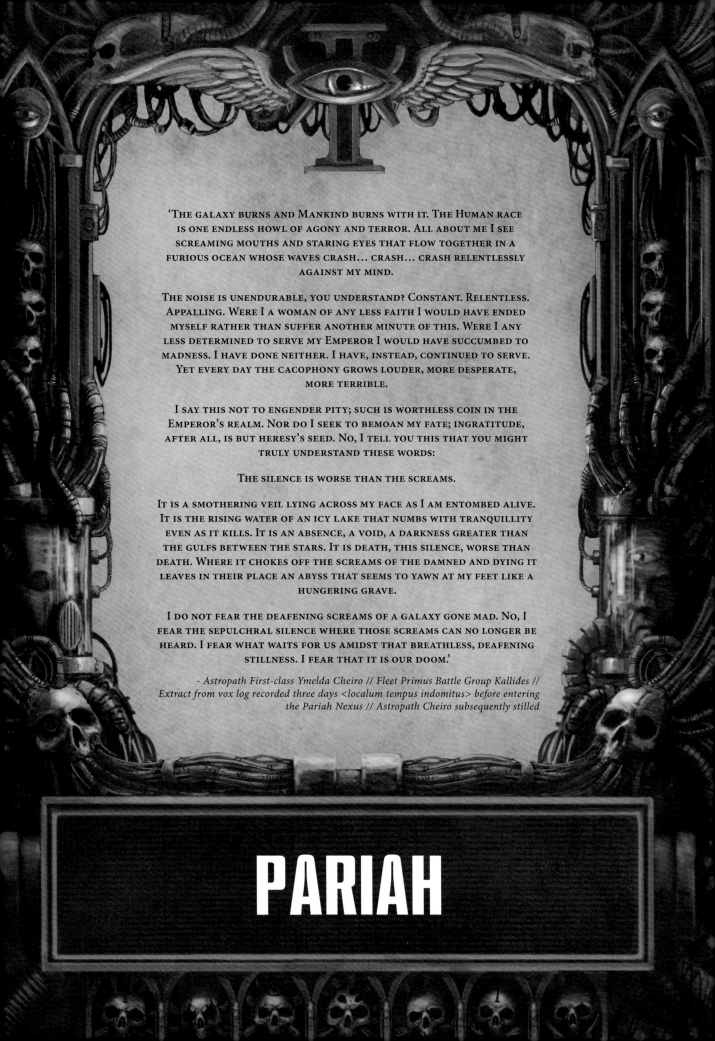

'The galaxy burns and Mankind burns with it. The Human race is one endless howl of agony and terror. All about me I see screaming mouths and staring eyes that flow together in a furious ocean whose waves crash... crash... crash relentlessly against my mind.

The noise is unendurable, you understand? Constant. Relentless. Appalling. Were I a woman of any less faith I would have ended myself rather than suffer another minute of this. Were I any less determined to serve my Emperor I would have succumbed to madness. I have done neither. I have, instead, continued to serve. Yet every day the cacophony grows louder, more desperate, more terrible.

I say this not to engender pity; such is worthless coin in the Emperor's realm. Nor do I seek to bemoan my fate; ingratitude, after all, is but heresy's seed. No, I tell you this that you might truly understand these words:

The silence is worse than the screams.

It is a smothering veil lying across my face as I am entombed alive. It is the rising water of an icy lake that numbs with tranquillity even as it kills. It is an absence, a void, a darkness greater than the gulfs between the stars. It is death, this silence, worse than death. Where it chokes off the screams of the damned and dying it leaves in their place an abyss that seems to yawn at my feet like a hungering grave.

I do not fear the deafening screams of a galaxy gone mad. No, I fear the sepulchral silence where those screams can no longer be heard. I fear what waits for us amidst that breathless, deafening stillness. I fear that it is our doom.'

- Astropath First-class Ymelda Cheiro // Fleet Primus Battle Group Kallides // Extract from vox log recorded three days <localum tempus indomitus> before entering the Pariah Nexus // Astropath Cheiro subsequently stilled

PARIAH

CONTENTS

PRODUCED BY THE WARHAMMER STUDIO

With thanks to the Mournival and the Infinity Circuit for their additional playtesting services

Games Workshop Ltd, Willow Rd, Lenton, Nottingham, NG7 2WS

games-workshop.com

INTRODUCTION

From the Ghoul Stars to the Veiled Region, the galaxy is engulfed in unnatural phenomena and ferocious warfare. Psychic mutation runs rife across Humanity's myriad worlds. The weft of realspace wears ever thinner as the unfettered madness of the warp strains to break through. Yet in the Nephilim Sector, all is silence…

When the Great Rift opened, its advent was a spur to anarchy and upheaval across the galaxy. The Imperium suffered terribly as waves of empyric corruption beat against its worlds, sowing mutation and madness through its peoples. Already perilous interplanetary travel and communication became more dangerous than ever as the warp's tides raged.

Mankind was far from the only species affected, however. The Cicatrix Maledictum spread its diseased light across every race in the galaxy, dragging each into the escalating mayhem in a different fashion. Ork Waaagh! after Ork Waaagh! was triggered as the greenskins' worlds were engulfed in warp storms and their psykers were tormented with visions of bellowing deities and galactic conquest. The

disparate Aeldari sought to harness the swelling tides of empyric energy, battle the unnatural warp-spawn they unleashed and prey upon those peoples already isolated and beset by catastrophe. Alien empires rose and fell. Everywhere the worshippers of the Dark Gods fought their way towards supremacy as reality itself teetered upon the brink of ultimate devastation.

Humanity's response took the form of the Indomitus Crusade. It saw battle group after battle group of warships and warriors push out into the darkness to reinforce their buckling defences. Yet Mankind was not alone in seeking to restore order. Deep in the Nephilim Sector the alien Necrons had instigated a plan of their own, a response so grand and merciless that only they could have concocted it.

IN THIS BOOK

This book is part of Psychic Awakening, an ongoing series set in the aftermath of the Great Rift. It contains an account of the first bloody war fought in the Pariah Nexus.

Inside you will find:
- The story of Humanity's horrific battles within the Pariah Nexus.
- A selection of missions to recreate key battles of this war.
- Updated rules for the Inquisition, including Warlord Traits, Relics and Stratagems.
- Rules and datasheets for several exciting new special characters, including the Daemonifuge and Lord Inquisitor Kyria Draxus.
- Rules for multiple Theatres of War ideal for recreating numerous conflicts from the Psychic Awakening series.

KALLIDES' QUEST

The Indomitus Crusade fleets were vast gatherings of military might, each with their own path to follow, each broken down into huge battle groups so as to spread their strength wide. Battle Group Kallides was one of the largest.

Indomitus Crusade Fleet Primus was one of several fleets to assemble around deep-void anchorages upon the fringes of the Sol System, and was undeniably the single largest and most powerful of all the initial Indomitus Crusade fleets. Boasting a full twenty-six battle groups – led out into the stars by Roboute Guilliman and Belisarius Cawl – Fleet Primus alone possessed the power to shake the very stars. This was no gross misallocation of materiel or act of vainglory on Guilliman's part, however; Fleet Primus' overall strategic mission was nothing less than the reinforcement and stabilisation of the entire Imperium Sanctus.

Much of Fleet Primus' initial efforts were angled towards the Segmentum Solar, for countless threats were to be found upon Terra's very threshold. Yet this was not true of all the fleet's battle groups. Some were charged instead with pushing outwards into the deeper dark of the war-torn Imperium Sanctus. Each was assigned a quest deemed vital to the overall success of the Indomitus Crusade, and to Roboute Guilliman's overall aim of shoring up and making safe the Imperium Sanctus. Battle Group Erastus, for example, was sent to crush the heretic war cults of the Ispolin Sub-sector before they could trigger a cascading warp breach and unleash legions of Daemons upon the systems to the galactic north of Terra. Battle Group Noctus was sent racing towards Armageddon, charged with a vital mission known only to Groupmaster LeVorne and her closest advisors. Then there was the battle group whose combined martial might was worth several of the smaller forces put together – Battle Group Kallides. Theirs would be a stranger road.

Many of the battle groups of Fleet Primus faced perils unleashed by the opening of the Great Rift. Empyric plagues, hordes of mutated monsters, invasions by the Heretic Astartes and uprisings by the deluded, the deranged or the daemonically possessed were all dangers encountered by Fleet Primus' battle groups as they pushed outward from the Sol System.

Certainly, as they advanced through the war-torn sub-sectors of the Imperium Sanctus, Battle Group Kallides met just such dangers. So ferociously disturbed was the sea of souls that they could travel only in short warp jumps. This ensured that the armies and warships of Battle Group Kallides had ample time to blood themselves against a myriad of heretic foes, for they could hardly be avoided. Yet this was not their true mission. Instead, Battle Group Kallides were charged with investigating the haunted region of absolute silence detected in the Nephilim Sub-sector.

THE DREAD ABSENCE

As the darkness of the Noctis Aeterna drew back, the distress calls of countless Imperial worlds rang out into the void. From the systems of the Nephilim Sub-sector, however, there was nothing but silence. It swiftly became apparent that the sheer absence of panicked screams or morbid lamentations was both unusual and deeply sinister; Crusade command dared not leave the shrouded region unexplored for fear of what terrors might be left unchecked to lurk there. At best, this was either a zone of space from which the darkness of the Noctis Aeterna refused to lift, or from which all Imperial life had been eradicated – phenomena in themselves that demanded further investigation. At worst, some other threat was simmering within the Zone of Silence to the galactic south of Badab and Nocturne. Something that had to be swiftly countered.

'You will be my champion in this. You will be the one who bears the light of Imperial vigilance into this dark and silent void. To you I entrust the advance guard of my grand Fleet Primus, in the certain knowledge that you will drive back the shadows and defeat whatever evils they conceal. To you I entrust this hope.'

- Roboute Guilliman to Groupmaster Marran

This, then, was the task of Battle Group Kallides, and it was one they were well equipped to discharge. It was led by Groupmaster Marran, an indomitable and unsubtle old Imperial Navy admiral known affectionately by his captains as 'the Bull Grox'. Mighty heroes of the Imperium formed Marran's war council and advised him in his campaigns, including lords of the Ultramarines, Black Templars and the Deathwatch, Nobles of Knightly Houses Terryn and Mortan, Princeps of the Legio Castigatum and the noted Ordo Xenos Inquisitor, Lord Kyria Draxus.

As they came at last to the systems bordering the Nephilim Sub-sector, the battle group's advance scouts reported panic and mayhem on a disturbing scale. Worlds lay in open revolt, their peoples neither seeking to throw off the yoke of Imperial oppression nor worship the Dark Gods, but to simply flee their planets en masse by whatever means possible. Seers filled vox channels with warnings of a smothering veil that turned the stars to darkness. In several systems, fierce wars raged against xenos invaders who fought with frantic intensity, not to seize the Emperor's worlds, but to flee further away from the Nephilim Sub-sector.

Diverting task forces to restore Imperial rule in the worst affected systems, Battle Group Kallides pushed ever closer to the zone of unnatural silence that their own Navigators and Astropaths could now sense ahead. The incautious may have been forgiven for believing this region a haven, for the maddened tides of the warp seemed to become as still as glass within its bounds. Yet the drifting defence monitors and unresponsive void stations encountered by Battle Group Kallides' ships told a different story. Steeling their courage, the force advanced into the region of silence, and their nightmare began in earnest.

DAEMONIFUGE

It was as Battle Group Kallides fought their way along the bloody road to the Zone of Silence that their forces were joined by a most unlikely – and for many, controversial – champion. Upon the world of Severitas, an isolated force of Battle Sisters from the Order of Our Martyred Lady were led to battle by Ephrael Stern, who some have named the Daemonifuge. Stern had been guided to her sisters by grim visions of a frozen, silent doom that she sought to prevent, and against which her Aeldari comrade Kyganil was even now gathering new allies. Stern joined the Battle Sisters' fight, unleashing her miraculous powers upon their Word Bearer foes. Though many amongst the Adepta Sororitas were initially reluctant to trust one whom the Inquisition had branded a witch, this demonstration of holy might convinced them of Stern's purity. Led by the Daemonifuge, the Battle Sisters won a crushing victory. Stern went with her sisters when they departed Severitas, recognising the Indomitus Crusade for the holy endeavour that it was, and seeking to aid it in any way she could. Yet, as Battle Group Kallides drew ever closer to the silent zone, Stern found her disquiet growing greater. Kyganil had not yet returned, and the Daemonifuge's grim visions became more vivid with each passing day.

TO LIGHT THE DARKNESS

Kallides was but one amongst hundreds of battle groups despatched from the Sol and Gehenna Systems during the initial Indomitus Crusade deployments. Each fleet had its own greater strategic mission, of which each battle group was but one component.

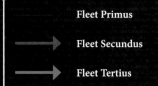

→	Fleet Primus
→	Fleet Secundus
→	Fleet Tertius

FLEET SECUNDUS

Lord Guilliman deemed that a strong counter-offensive was required to draw the attention of the Chaos forces while the wider Imperium regained its footing. So did Fleet Secundus take the Martyr's Road towards the Eye of Terror itself.

FLEET PRIMUS

The third to actually set out, Primus was the largest Indomitus Crusade fleet and possessed the widest strategic remit. Directed by Roboute Guilliman and Belisarius Cawl themselves, the fleet's many battle groups spread out through the ravaged systems of the Imperium Sanctus, seeking to stabilise those parts of the Emperor's realm still known to stand firm and loyal. Only once such a foundation was established could any notion of a fight back be considered.

THE EYE OF TERROR

VIGILUS

CHINCHARE

CADIA

BELIS CORONA

PISCINA

AGRIPINAA

NACHMUND GAUNTLET

HYDRAPHUR

ARMAGEDDON

ELYSIA

CICATRIX MALEDICTUM

SEGMENTUM SOLAR

LASTRATI

GOLGOTHA

VORDRAST

SEGMENTUM PACIFICUS

TERRA & MARS

RYZA

THE MAELSTROM

CATACHAN

GATHALAMOR

BATTLE GROUP KALLIDES

NECROMUNDA

BADAB

ULTIMA MACHARIA

MACHARIA

KRIEG

LUTHER McINTYRE

TALLARN

CHIROS

UHULIS SECTOR

OPHELIA

NOCTURNE

BALOR

V'RUN

SIREN'S STORM

PARIAH NEXUS

ALEUSIS

BANE'S LANDING

FLEET TERTIUS

First to slip its leash, Fleet Tertius surged straight from the Sol System's orbital muster and into battle across the region known as Machorta Sound. Having conquered the Khornate forces that she met there, Fleetmaster VanLeskus then took her charges on into the deep darkness of the Segmentum Pacificus, her mission to pierce its depths, then swing to the galactic south and into the Segmentum Tempestus in turn.

SOLSTICE

RYNN'S WORLD

NEPHILIM SECTOR

SEGMENTUM TEMPESTUS

REDUCTUS SECTOR

AGRAX

BAKKA

ANTAGONIS

SAN LEOR

GRYPHONNE IV

ILLUSTRIS

THE VEILED REGION

THE PARIAH NEXUS

To the Imperial forces piercing its veil of silence, the region they would eventually come to call the Pariah Nexus appeared ineffable and insidious. Yet to its Necron architects the contra-immaterian nodal matrix – as they called it – was an unparalleled work of cosmic engineering.

At the heart of the Nexus lay the Xendu System, where an immense noctilith cage had been constructed to trammel its vast and ferocious star. Myriad Necron structures hung in the void about this cyclopean cage, anchored to it by coruscating beams of energy. Flight upon flight of tomb ships and trans-atmospheric fighter craft flitted around through the searing light of the imprisoned star, watching over their vast charge.

Further out lay networks of vast blackstone pylons – their deployment extending through patterns of non-Euclidean fractal crypto-logic that would have driven the greatest mortal minds mad. Scattered through nodal and outlier systems, each pylon was a unique and remarkable structure of colossal size whose purpose was to sustain and extend a field of negatively charged anti-empyric energies.

This, then, was the immense hyper-structure that the Imperium came to know as the Pariah Nexus. The mysteries of its operation lay far beyond the ken of even the Adeptus Mechanicus' inquisitive techno-clergy, but its effects were unmistakable. Within days of Battle Group Kallides piercing the Nexus, they discovered the horrific phenomenon known as the Stilling. Matters grew darker from there...

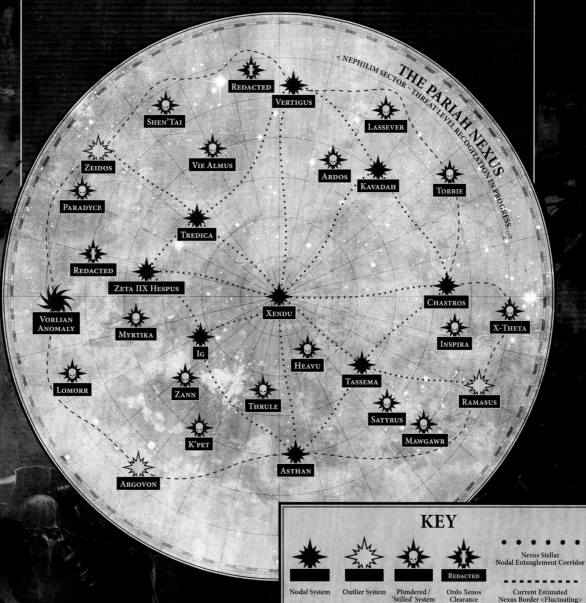

< NEPHILIM SECTOR – THREAT LEVEL RECOGITATION IN PROGRESS... >

THE PARIAH NEXUS

REDACTED
VERTIGUS
SHEN'TAI
LASSEVER
ZEIDOS
VIE ALMUS
ARDOS
KAVADAH
TORBIE
PARADYCE
TREDICA
REDACTED
ZETA IIX HESPUS
CHASTROS
VORLIAN ANOMALY
XENDU
X-THETA
MYRTIKA
INSPIRA
IG
HEAVU
TASSEMA
LOMORR
RAMASUS
ZANN
THRULE
SATYRUS
MAWGAWR
K'PET
ASTHAN
ARGOVON

KEY

| Nodal System | Outlier System | Plundered / 'Stilled' System | REDACTED Ordo Xenos Clearance Crimson | Nexus Stellar Nodal Entanglement Corridor | Current Estimated Nexus Border <Fluctuating> |

BEYOND THE VEIL

No visible phenomena marked the silent zone, at least not within realspace. Yet the Navigators of Battle Group Kallides spoke in awed tones of a shimmering psychic veil, like a wall of mist expanding gradually outwards. What lay beyond they could not say, except that they sensed a strange calming of the furious warp.

Several amongst Groupmaster Marran's staff advised caution, but Marran would not hear of it. He had been entrusted by Roboute Guilliman himself to peel back the shadows that hid this region. Direct as always, Marran would halt neither for inquisitive tech-magi – desiring to study the empyric phenomena – nor for the more superstitious of his captains, who warned of void spirits and ill fortune lurking ahead. With increasingly ferocious warp storms threatening to smash the battle group's ships apart, Marran ordered his Navigators to brave the stable empyric currents that passed through the shimmering veil. He could only hope that what lay beyond would prove to be a safe harbour.

Beyond the shrouding warp mists, the Imperial ships sailed into a region of deathly calm. Some of the battle group's psykers claimed that the warp itself had been brought to a millpond stillness. Others attested to perceiving the seething tides of the empyrean still raging, but trapped impotent beyond the walls of a fractally complex crystal dome. Others still whispered that the battle group had sailed into some dread immaterial mausoleum upon which a silken shroud had fallen. They moaned that, even now, the dust of their own imminent demise settled about them in drifts.

Groupmaster Marran ordered a broadly spread advance into the silent zone from the galactic north-west, distributing task forces so that the Imperial front pushed in towards the systems of Paradyce, Zeidos, Shen'Tai and Vertigus. Each prong of the advance reported a deep sense of disquiet settling across its soldiery. Navigators, Astropaths and battle psykers alike complained of being stifled and disoriented, struggling to grasp for powers that had previously come as naturally as thought. Tech-magi warned of warp engines labouring, requiring more and more power to propel the Imperial warships forward; Magos Enginarius Khasio, of Marran's own flagship the *Hammerblow*, compared the matter to a Martian dune yacht whose silka-glass sails had not even the slightest puff of wind to fill them. Panic filled the corridors of the *Enduring Hatred*, the *Rapacious*

and the *Emperor's Mercy* as their Geller fields burst like Human bodies ejected suddenly into the depressurising void of space. Yet no Daemons fell upon the unprotected crews of those hapless craft; some called it a miracle, but others eyed one another fearfully, unsettled by catastrophe's absence.

Struggling to perform each warp jump and beset by eerie faults, the warships of Battle Group Kallides forged sluggishly on. Vox officers, masters of auspex and increasingly ill-looking Astropaths scoured the void for the slightest sign of Imperial presence. The systems towards which they travelled should have been heavily settled yet, though they detected the binharic chatter of automated machine spirits, there was no sign of Human life. Vox channels and astropathic conduits were silent. Void traffic was non-existent. Worse still, strange energy signatures were detected pulsing out from multiple Imperial worlds. Each was so powerful that it could be felt thousands of miles into deep space, yet their nature – or what they portended – could not be discerned.

Matters became stranger and more horrible as the ground forces landed upon the first of the silent worlds. The malaise afflicting the battle group's warriors increased its hold, especially amongst the numerous Astra Militarum regiments. Soldiers complained of feeling watched and anxious, only to succumb hours or days later to growing lethargy, exhaustion and despair. Executions by Commissars reached epidemic proportions as Imperial Guard soldiery abandoned their posts, spoke of giving up, or simply collapsed, unresponsive and unwilling to move again. Psykers were still more terribly stricken. Many complained of being smothered, as though gasping painfully beneath a torrent of water from which they could never truly catch their breath. Others

went mad, some taking their own lives, and soon the battle group's complement of Navigators and Astropaths had become dangerously depleted. Marran ordered all surviving psykers to be assigned vigilant bodyguards, whose duty it was to protect the tortured mutants from themselves, as much as from any external threat.

Nor were the Adeptus Astartes, the scions of the Knight Houses or the servants of the Omnissiah unaffected by what soon became known as the Stilling; they were more resistant, but not altogether immune. Only the battle group's Adepta Sororitas appeared largely untouched.

The condition of the worlds within the silent zone did not help morale – agri-complexes, spaceports, generatorums, refineries, mining settlements, fortifications and even entire cities stood empty. The Imperial forces found food cold and mouldering at tables, as though abandoned mid-meal. Servitors stood dead-eyed and silent, their machinery still operational, but their living components seized. Groundcars, mining rigs and shuttles lay where they had crashed, as though their pilots had lost control but done nothing to prevent collision. In places, much damage had been done by fires raging out of control, or plasma generators overloading. There were signs of battle, too, but they were few and faint, their origins hard to discern. It was as though billions of the Emperor's servants had simply vanished, leaving possessions and duties abandoned in their wake.

Lord Inquisitor Draxus led the effort to discover what had occurred upon the stilled worlds. Surely the same malaise afflicting the battle group's warriors must also have claimed these people.

Noctilith, commonly known as blackstone, is a substance dimly understood. True, we know that the infamous pylons of lamented Cadia were formed from this substance. We know also that they were subjected to thousands of years of somewhat esoteric study by an unending parade of magi, crypto-scholars and even Inquisitorial agents. Yet it seems that, for all of their posturing, arcane accoutrements and florid terminology, even the most exceptionally wise and well-resourced individuals learned only that they had ever more questions to ask. Some have asserted – rightly or wrongly, it is hard to say – that this substance is linked in some fashion to the stuff of the warp, perhaps even that it resonates with or against the tides of the sea of souls. If this is so, I have seen no direct evidence to corroborate the claim. Yet none can deny that when the pylons of Cadia fell, so too did the Great Rift open. I am too old and too cynical to believe in coincidences anymore. Now we see the Necrons raising pylons of their own, and fashioned from that same substance. What can it all mean? I do not know, but I steel myself against the possible answers…

- Xenosavant Hesper Iax

How they had vanished she could not answer, and every interrogation of data-spirits and vid-logs revealed only corrupted files and erased surveillance spools. Lord Inquisitor Draxus had her suspicions about the origins of these horrors. Indeed, she had harboured concerns even before joining Battle Group Kallides, yet she required more proof.

THE MESMOCH PYLON

As the Imperial forces pressed on, they were unaware that alien agents observed their every move. From within pocket dimensions and through unimaginably powerful disoccluder engines, the glowing, android eyes of the Necrons saw all. Dispassionately they watched, but

did not strike. Their master – or he who spoke on behalf of their master – had commanded them not to. Instead, they transmitted every observation back through quantum entanglement channels, to where Illuminor Szeras lurked like a spider at the heart of his vast web. The Illuminor watched with insectile fascination as the Humans struggled beneath the influence of what the Necrons termed their contra-immaterean nodal matrix. Soon it would be time to attack, he knew, but for now Szeras would continue his observations.

The trigger for war came when a Vanguard strike force of Ultramarines made planetfall on Mesmoch in the Zeidos System. Sent to investigate anomalous energy readings from within the planet's partially settled jungles, the scions of Ultramar found a towering pylon wrought from blackstone. The structure was several miles in circumference, and so tall that clouds whirled unnaturally around its tip, which scraped the planet's troposphere. The Ultramarines had no difficulty in immediately identifying that the strange structures clustered around the pylon's base were Necron in origin. Nor could they mistake the bludgeoning waves of entropic energy rolling steadily from the structure that left them struggling to act.

Act they did, however, by gathering strategic intelligence on the pylon and its sprawling defences. Held back by Szeras' restraining protocols, the structure's defenders could not pursue the Ultramarines as they made their escape; by the time the Illuminor realised that his hand had been forced, it was too late. The Humans had discovered the source of their suffering, and they would not be long in striking at it.

The Mesmoch Pylon was the first of its kind to be discovered, but it was far

from the last. Groupmaster Marran received word of further pylons – each similar but distinctly different from one another – located upon other Imperial worlds in the region. Reports came in, also, of Necron armies on the move; several task forces had met sudden and ferocious resistance by Necron phalanxes that appeared as if from nowhere. Casualties were mounting and alarm was spreading rapidly, yet Marran would not be distracted; he had a target at last, and he was determined to prove to his demoralised followers that this mysterious enemy could be fought.

The assault upon the Mesmoch Pylon went poorly from the start. Warp drive failures and stilled crews meant that only two-thirds of the requested warships and troop carriers reached Marran's mustering point in time. Where before the Zeidos System had been lifeless, now formations of darkly glittering Necron warships swept from the void to oppose the Imperial attack.

Many Human warships were damaged and several destroyed by the time Marran's forces reached Mesmoch. The formerly silent world now blazed with eldritch light as unveiled orbital defences spat fire into the void. Shields flaring and hulls blazing, Imperial carriers disgorged waves of infantry onto Mesmoch's surface. The Adeptus Astartes led the attack with Ultramarines, zealous Black Templars and several Deathwatch kill teams carving out beachheads to the north and east of the pylon. Six entire regiments of Astra Militarum infantry and armour followed, while the immense lander of the Warlord Titan *Deus Redemptor* thundered down in their midst.

Necron phalanxes marched out to oppose the attack; Canoptek constructs and rank on rank of Warriors pushed through the rain-slicked jungles. Bolts, las-light and artillery shells criss-crossed with

flaying beams of gauss energy and actinic tesla blasts, ripping foliage to blazing shreds as Imperial and xenos forces clashed along several fronts. Meanwhile, the Apocalypse-class battleship *Triumph* bullied its way through the hostile void to draw bombardment solutions upon the pylon itself. The heavens lit white as the *Triumph*'s lance batteries and nova cannon let fly, and cheers rose from the Imperial lines as the pylon vanished amidst a sea of fire and smoke. As the air cleared, however, the pylon could be seen rising undamaged from amidst the burning jungle, the structures at its base safe beneath flickering quantum shields.

Ground attack, then, seemed the only way to assail the Mesmoch Pylon, yet this too was proving increasingly untenable. The Adeptus Astartes had carved a path to within a half mile of the pylon's base. However, the Imperial Guard were faltering beneath its numbing influence – more soldiers losing heart or collapsing glassy-eyed with each passing moment. Seeing their

enemies' weakness, the Necrons unleashed a wave of potent war engines from within the pyramidal structures around the pylon's base. Hovering monoliths blasted stalled Leman Russ tanks and overmatched squads of Inceptors with lashing bolts of energy. Doomsday Barges spat searing beams that reduced Intercessors and Assault Marines to glowing ash. Battered by hostile fire, the *Deus Redemptor*'s void shields collapsed, and the Titan reeled under hammering blasts of eldritch fire.

Only the martial might and unwavering discipline of the Space Marines prevented defeat from becoming a rout. Squad by squad they staged a fighting retreat, providing rearguard cover as the dispirited Imperial forces limped back towards their extraction zones. The names of kill teams Amaeus and Thannyr entered the annals of glory as their battle-brothers died to the last to hold the Necrons back. A ferocious counter-attack, led by Marshal Ghehart of the Black Templars, repulsed Necron forces

seeking to finish off the wounded *Deus Redemptor,* and saw brutal injuries incurred by both sides. By the time the Imperial landing craft were screaming skywards through whirling flights of Doom Scythes and Tomb Blades, the ground forces they bore to safety had suffered crippling casualties. There could be no hiding it. The assault on Mesmoch had been a crushing, humiliating defeat, one that Battle Group Kallides could ill afford to repeat.

> '**How many of these pylons have our enemies raised? How do we effect their downfall? Emperor guide me, for I walk in the darkness and, though my faith remains unbroken, I fear I cannot see my path back to the light…**'
>
> *- Groupmaster Marran, personal prayers following Mesmoch Assault*

THE BATTLE OF THE GATES

Where before this region of stilled worlds had been a silent and mysterious puzzle, suddenly it was a lethal war zone alive with threats. As more Necron forces emerged to challenge the Imperial invaders, the situation began to look desperate indeed.

In the wake of the disaster on Mesmoch, Battle Group Kallides reeled. Dragged down by the sapping influence of the Necrons' strange new weapon, and smashed on multiple battlefields by the android xenos' armies, the Imperial forces teetered upon the brink of catastrophic collapse.

Setting aside his personal dismay, Groupmaster Marran mobilised reserve divisions and tried to recall the more far-flung of his task forces. Astropathic attempts to reach the systems beyond the veil came to naught; one exhausted, half-mad psyker described their experience as trying to shout in a nightmare, but being able to produce nothing more than a strangled wheeze. Instead, swift messenger ships were despatched back along the battle group's trail, though whether their warp engines would function or their Navigators would be able to guide them from the becalmed zone was in great doubt.

On Vie Almus Majora, Kalliphor and Paradyce IV, Imperial armies suffered further punishing defeats as the Necrons' numbers doubled and redoubled. The faded panoply of numerous dynasties, both major and minor, were identified by Imperial strategos – such a widespread alliance of the ancient xenos' factions had never been witnessed before. Defeat followed defeat, but at least in one thing Battle Group Kallides made swift gains; they had now confirmed the presence of blackstone pylons on enough planets to know for certain that whatever eldritch curse afflicted this region, the Necrons were using those ineffable structures to generate it. It was at this time that the term Pariah Nexus was coined for the region, for the horrifying effects afflicting the Human forces were all too similar to those caused by the presence of the soulless mutants known as nulls. The name was apposite, but did little to aid morale. Such beings were figures of fear to the great mass of Humanity, and evoking such bogeymen at so desperate an hour only saw fear and panic grow yet more pronounced.

Amidst this atmosphere of superstitious terror and panic, Ephrael Stern came before Groupmaster Marran in person. The Daemonifuge requested a chance to restore Imperial spirits by leading a counter-attack. Stern had chosen her target well; not one of the massively fortified pylon worlds, but rather a major Necron transportation hub where Vanguard scouts had found three dolmen gates clustered together on one site. It was still a heavily defended locale, but if it could be conquered then the flow of Necron phalanxes into the war zones of the Shen'Tai and Zeidos Systems would be choked off at a stroke.

Marran could see the merit of Stern's plan. Moreover, he had heard accounts of the Adepta Sororitas resisting the Pariah Nexus' effects where even the Adeptus Astartes had struggled. Offering private prayer to the Emperor for a miracle, Marran put his faith in Stern and approved the largest offensive since Mesmoch. It was a substantial gamble; another defeat on that scale would see Battle Group Kallides brought to its knees.

According to Imperial records, the target world was called Cherist. It was located in the Lomorr System, far to the galactic south of all previous battle group operations. By the time Stern's allotted Task Force VII had laboured their way to their destination through the becalmed immaterium, they were far beyond the aid of Marran's remaining forces. The attack would have to succeed or fail entirely on its own merit.

Cherist was a viciously arctic planet, languishing far from the warmth of its star. Though it troubled the Necrons little, the world's low light, killing cold, shard-like blizzards and unpredictable nitrogen geysers promised a perilous war zone for the Imperial attackers. Yet they did not baulk; led by Missions of the Order of Our Martyred Lady and the Order of the Bloody Rose, the task force's armies swept down upon the frozen world.

Ephrael Stern led her invasion force against the dolmen gate complex located at Cherist's south pole.

Two vast invasion cathedrums thundered down through the planet's screaming snowstorms, accompanied by the heavy landing keeps of the Knights of House Mortan as they began the attack.

The Necron complex sprawled as large as a city, its structures rising out of the ice-locked bedrock around the feet of a towering mountain. Outlier complexes jutted from the rocky pinnacles of the mountain's foothills, each boasting formidable defensive weapons that had to be eliminated for the attack to succeed. The gates themselves, meanwhile, were clustered amidst a monolithic tangle of xenotech structures dug into the mountain's feet, wreathed in layers of protective quantum shielding.

The only viable route of approach was up a wide valley, dotted with outcroppings of ruined Imperial structures and open to attack from all sides. This, then, was the route that the Adepta Sororitas and their supporting Astra Militarum forces would have to take, but that did not mean that they had to walk heedless into the teeth of enemy guns.

The Imperial attack began with a ferocious barrage as the descending invasion cathedrums rained fire upon the Necron complex. Knowing that their enemies' fortifications were well shielded,

they instead hammered the mountainside itself. Megatons of explosive ordnance gouged yawning rents in the mountain's flanks. Rock and ice shrapnel filled the air as vast slabs of stone broke away and thundered down in a crushing avalanche. Unshielded Necron structures were pummelled to ruin, whilst even the more well-defended fortifications were half-buried by vast spoil-heaps of rubble and shattered ice.

In answer to this spectacular opening salvo, the Necrons' defences came alive. Bolts of coruscating energy leapt from weapons pylons and shimmering defence menhirs to scourge the flanks of the Imperial craft. One of the Mortan landing keeps was reduced to a tumbling fireball that spiralled away from the Imperial drop-formation and hit the distant snowfields with meteoric force. At the same time, rank after glittering rank of Necron Warriors and war engines spilled from tomb structures like insects defending their briskly kicked hive.

The Imperial landing craft came down regardless. One invasion cathedrum rumbled low over the mountain's lower slopes and, as it did, streaks of fire fell from its underside. Two dozen squads of Seraphim and Zephyrim swept down upon the mountainside and began a perilous, bounding advance towards the half-buried rear defences of the Necron fortress. The Knights' landing craft slammed down amidst the rocky foothills, their passengers striding forth like folkloric giants to strike at the outlying Necron artillery bases.

Meanwhile, Stern herself descended from one of hundreds of dropships and bulk landers to lead the massed push up the valley's throat. She marched at the head of more than two thousand Sisters of the Order of Our Martyred Lady and another five hundred from the Order of the Bloody Rose. They advanced into the ice shard ridden snows with their braziers blazing and their voices raised in war hymns, while alongside them came several thousand infantry and battle tanks of the Astra Militarum. Every Imperial Guardsman present feared the dread influence of the Stilling, yet despite the freezing cold, each man and woman amongst them felt the Battle Sisters' faith blazing in their own chests. They knew that, with these holy warriors of the Emperor at their head, they could win this fight.

The leader of the Nihilakh Necron garrison was less convinced of that fact. Known for his utter disdain of the lesser races, Phaeron Shemvokh had responded to this invasion, not with panic or horror, but with indignant outrage. How dare these flesh vermin besmirch his holdings with their presence? How dare they attack their betters? These were

the questions burning through Shemvokh's artificial synapses as he mounted his Catacomb Command Barge and led his legions out in person to meet the assault.

Necron Warriors marched down the valley in their thousands, gauss fire licking from their guns to flay the interlopers alive. Tomb Blades shot through the swirling snows, their strafing fire spinning Battle Sisters off their feet and reducing Imperial Basilisks and Wyverns to blazing wrecks. Heavier Necron war engines drifted in their wake, looming up through the swirling snows to unleash searing blasts of cosmic energy into the Imperial advance. Drifting ash and roiling steam joined the ice shards as entire squads of Battle Sisters and Imperial Guardsmen were annihilated with each bolt. Meanwhile, at the battle's heart, Phaeron Shemvokh led the march of his elite Lychguard,

intending to carve a path through the Human ranks and tear their battle line contemptuously in two.

Stern saw all of this developing, from Knights duelling defence pylons with explosive fury to Imperial warriors and Necron terrors locked in furious battle, and she prayed with ever greater fervour for the Emperor's intercession. Surely now her visions must come to pass and Kyganil would bring the might of the Ynnari to aid her in this crucial moment. Stern had her own reasons for assaulting a location where trammelled sections of the webway connected with realspace. For a moment, she believed that all was beginning to align as she saw the distinctive flare of the gates activating. Yet, to her horror, it was Necron reinforcements that marched through them, not infiltrating Aeldari.

One moment, Ephrael Stern fought alongside only her sisters, all of them battling amidst the whirling snow and smoke against the relentlessly advancing Necrons. The next moment, her Aeldari comrade was at her side.

'Kyganil! How do you come here?' she asked, then, with a leaden weight coalescing in her chest. 'Where are the Ynnari?'

'It has been a long and bloody road that I have walked since last we spoke, one that brought me by dark ways through the gates of this world,' Kyganil replied. Even as he spoke, the bruised and bloodied Aeldari plied his blades amongst the Necrons. Android bodies fell sparking and twitching before phasing from sight, and the outcast nodded to himself with satisfaction.

'They are not coming to our aid, are they?' Stern asked, weaving aside from a searing green blast and unloading her pistol into a Necron's grinning skull face.

'I sought my kin, as the prophetess instructed,' Kyganil replied. 'I led the cursed one to the place of meetings and so aided the huntress' banishment. Yet even in victory, there was defeat. Even in triumph, discord. Khaine's road forks and forks again beneath the feet of they who serve death in war, and it seeks to drown them in the blood they shed. Even had they wished to bring their aid to this place they could not have done so, and when last I saw the prophetess she told me that, in this hour at least, she could not follow the red road hence.'

Stern shook her head, forgoing her curse of all xenos only for Kyganil's sake. She looked around at the battle raging on all sides, the courageous Human warriors pouring fire into their advancing enemies and howling prayers to the heavens even as the enemy flayed, disintegrated and burned them alive.

'We do not need their aid,' she said, her voice as cold and certain as the endless winter of this blighted world. 'We have faith, and with that we shall shake the stars themselves!'

DELIVERANCE

It was in this moment, as the battle turned against the Imperial invaders, that the centremost dolmen gate exploded with tremendous force. A great cheer rose up from the Imperial lines, redoubling as the last surviving Seraphim and Zephyrim darted away from the gate's wreckage, haloes of holy power shining about them as they continued to fight. Stern saw their example and knew that she could do no less. It would not fall to some band of aliens to win this victory for the Imperium; the Emperor's servants had their faith and their fury, and by those weapons would this war be won!

With that thought, Ephrael Stern's full power was unleashed. Hair and cloak flying and eyes shining with white fire, the Daemonifuge rose into the air at the battle's heart with the wings of the Aquila spread around her, wrought in lightning and flame. Where that light burned, even those who had stilled rose again, their eyes clearing, while those who had flagged drove forward with blades flashing and

battle cries on their lips. Phaeron Shemvokh watched, nonplussed, for surely the Crypteks' strange dampening field was supposed to prevent just such manifestations of psychic power? He could not know or comprehend that it was holy faith, not warp-spawned puissance, that enabled this miracle to manifest. The Imperial warriors understood well enough, however; their prayers and hymnals swelled defiantly as Stern's energies lashed blazing rents through the Necron lines, sending a second dolmen gate toppling in flames.

Imperious, the Phaeron commanded his legions to redouble their attack. Yet, to his amazement, it was the beleaguered Imperial forces instead who surged forward to overrun his front ranks. The ground shook as the surviving Imperial Knights stormed down from high ground to hit the

Necrons from both sides, while at the same moment Ephrael Stern and Kyganil swept down upon Phaeron Shemvokh. The duel that followed was ferocious. Bolts of light leapt from Shemvokh's staff as his Lychguard hacked and stabbed at their attackers, with skill honed over aeons. Yet they could not halt Stern's fury, nor the cold hatred of Kyganil. One by one the Lychguard fell, until at last Shemvokh's barge was blasted from the sky by holy lightning, his magnificent body reduced to smoking wreckage.

The fighting raged on for another hour after the Phaeron's fall, but with resurgent faith within the Imperial ranks, and the Necron command structure in tatters, the result of the battle was never in question from that moment onward. By the time the last of the dolmen gates was smashed and the structures around them demolished by the point-blank fire of the Knights, one thing was clear – faith was a weapon that the Imperium could use to counter the Necrons' awful entropic weapon. Battle Group Kallides might yet prevail.

INTO THE TOMB

Following the Imperial victory on Cherist, the war in the Pariah Nexus entered a new phase. Battle group command recognised the pivotal role that faith would now play in their plans. Adepta Sororitas, Black Templars and countless Imperial preachers came to the fore, their zealous convictions bolstering their comrades' efforts.

Illuminor Szeras was intrigued by the Humans' resistance to the contra-immaterean nodal matrix. He and his Crypteks laboured tirelessly, dissecting specimens from myriad battlefields as they tried to understand what psychic discipline the Humans were employing. Their victims' claims of miracles and faith were discarded as primitive prattle. The Necrons had met their gods, after all, and shattered them; they would not believe that the deities of the lesser races had the power to resist where the C'tan had failed!

While Szeras plied his science, the war raged on – the Vie Almus Majora counter-push, the Death March of Paradyce II, the Battle of Vorlian Wash – each conflict saw the Imperial forces resurgent. The effects of the Pariah Nexus were lessened – but by no means halted – by the warding power of faith. Moreover, aided by vast congregations of fanatical preachers who packed their decks and whipped their crews into a frenzy, several messenger ships had escaped the Pariah Nexus and returned with the pacification task forces in tow.

As yet however, the Imperial forces had not managed to damage a single Necron pylon, and were no closer to understanding their purpose or operation. With much of the battle group focused simply on holding the Necron legions at bay, it fell to Lord Inquisitor Kyria Draxus to lead this esoteric, but crucial, aspect of the war.

THE TREDICA EXPEDITION

Poring over reams of strategic, prophetic and xenoarchaeological reports, Lady Draxus settled upon the Tredica System as her target. Located deep within the Nexus, it had been scouted by Task Force VII, of whom only a single, barely coherent squad of Tempestus Scions had returned. Yet they had brought with them a wealth of pict-captures, augury and helm-cam footage that revealed three worlds dragged from their alignment to hang around an immense, night-black artefact in the void. Energy signatures suggested that at least one pylon was present upon each of the three worlds, while the survivors' harrowing accounts provided Draxus with further

details of the interiors of several xenos tombs. Whatever the vast void-artefact was, it was the most significant structure in the Nexus yet encountered, and Kyria Draxus wished to plunder its secrets.

The Inquisitor hand-picked her expedition; designated Task Force XIV, it was comprised of Deathwatch, Black Templars, Battle Sisters, Tempestus Scions and a conclave of tech-magi from the forge world of Stygies VIII. They would go to Tredica, not with any foolhardy hope of destroying the system's pylons, but rather of gaining the intelligence that might allow Battle Group Kallides to understand the ominous alien structures, and so defeat them.

The Tempestus Scions that had escaped Tredica held a secret, however. Illuminor Szeras, who also sought answers, had implanted them with mindshackle scarabs before their release. He reasoned that whatever champions the Humans sent to Tredica, they would be excellent subjects for interrogation. Their knowledge, Szeras hoped, would allow him to at last exterminate the Human

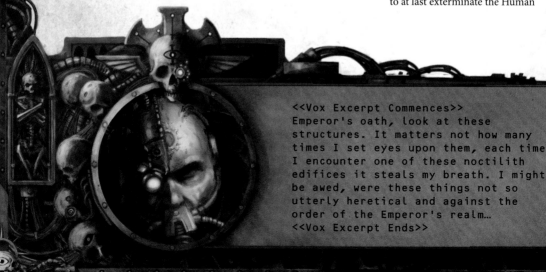

```
<<Vox Excerpt Commences>>
Emperor's oath, look at these
structures. It matters not how many
times I set eyes upon them, each time
I encounter one of these noctilith
edifices it steals my breath. I might
be awed, were these things not so
utterly heretical and against the
order of the Emperor's realm...
<<Vox Excerpt Ends>>
```

infestation. The Illuminor's master awaited confirmation of the nodal matrix's success; any pitiful resistance from the Human vermin needed to be swiftly and mercilessly stamped out. In this Szeras had erred; Kyria Draxus had seen the effects of mindshackle scarabs before and recognised the trap. Thus, she was going in not only with her eyes open, but accompanied by a military asset she did not believe the Necrons could possibly account for – Ephrael Stern.

By the time Task Force XIV reached the Tredica System they had lost one of their ships to the becalmed warp tides and been forced to fight several skirmishes with marauding Necron forces. Regardless, the task force immediately swept into action; Marshal Kurtz of the Black Templars led a diversionary raid against the world of Tredica Decitor, while a combined strike of Battle Sisters and Tempestus Scions fell upon the strange xenotech platforms orbiting above Tredica Fortis. Once auspexes confirmed that Necron warships and defence phalanxes were moving to engage these two feints, Draxus led her own force in the true strike at Tredica Ardaxis. This was the largest of the three worlds slaved to the ominous void-obelisk; it was this world that gave off the strongest energy signatures in the system, and from here that the scarab-enslaved Tempestus Scions had 'escaped'.

Tredica Ardaxis had been a prosperous hive world the Necrons' galactic engineering had subjected the planet to terrible stresses. Its

ruptured atmosphere was fouled by the ash and fume of ferocious volcanic eruptions, and its once proud hives were now shattered mass graves.

Three Necron pylons of colossal size rose from the planet's surface; one from its frozen night side, another from its scorched day side, and the third and largest from the hazy band of the planet's time-locked terminator. It was towards this pylon that Draxus' Inquisitorial cruiser, *Paladin's Shadow,* crept. Tredica Ardaxis was also watched over by Necron orbitals, but the nimble ship slipped beneath the muzzles of their guns seemingly undetected. Perhaps this was due to the cruiser's unusual shields, which were based on Aeldari holo-field technology. Privately, Kyria Draxus thought it more likely that their progress was being permitted. Regardless, she would exploit this laxity and be ready for whatever came next.

Paladin's Shadow settled into orbit a bare handful of miles from the peak of the pylon, which was so vast that it rose into the void. So close, the pylon's effects were punishing; preachers patrolled the decks and corridors in thronging mobs, their howled prayers and sanctified incense intended to shield the crew from the threat of stilling.

Sleek gunships slid from the cruiser's bays, as shielded as their parent craft. They shot down towards the tomb structures that glowed in the twilight around the pylon's base. The structure rose from a hive city's butchered shell, and all on board the gunships felt anger at what the Necrons had done to this world. There was no sign of the foe as the gunships touched down and disgorged Draxus' force of Deathwatch Space Marines, Battle Sisters and tech-magi aboard their armoured personnel carriers.

As the gunships dusted off, however, Illuminor Szeras sprang his trap. Shimmering green portals unfurled, and from them shrieked flights of Doom Scythes and Night Scythes. The former shot through the retreating Imperial gunships, sending several spiralling down in flames. The Night Scythes, meanwhile, ran their invasion beams across the ruins surrounding Draxus' force. Where before there had been only ashen rubble and blackened corpses, now there stood an elite force of Necron Immortals and Lychguard, arrayed in a noose about the Imperial force. Kyria Draxus recognised the spindle-

Today I have discovered a most useful band of allies hidden away within the masses of Battle Group Kallides. I was already aware that tech-magi from the forge world of Stygies VIII formed part of this force. What I had not appreciated was that their entire cabal are in fact Xenarites. I think it best not to commit to data log how I discovered the true allegiance of these tech-magi; suffice it to say that they will prove tremendously useful now that I know of their beliefs and the breadth of their xenotechnological knowledge. They will aid me, of course; for one thing, even the priests of the Machine God would not lightly cross an Inquisitor. Furthermore, were someone to let slip about their beliefs and predilection for the study of alien technologies, it would see them persecuted – lethally so – by the more conservative elements of the battle group. Yet I prefer willing allies to those coerced, and in this I have them precisely where I want them. How could they resist the secrets of Tredica Ardaxis, after all? +++KD//log entry 5646// END+++

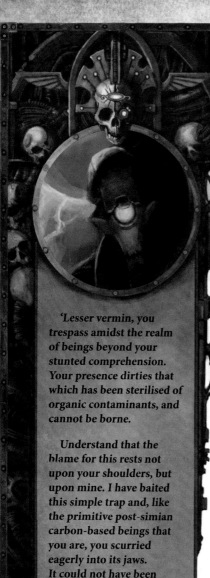

'Lesser vermin, you trespass amidst the realm of beings beyond your stunted comprehension. Your presence dirties that which has been sterilised of organic contaminants, and cannot be borne.

Understand that the blame for this rests not upon your shoulders, but upon mine. I have baited this simple trap and, like the primitive post-simian carbon-based beings that you are, you scurried eagerly into its jaws. It could not have been otherwise.

The fear, the confusion and the aggression that you are feeling, these are all natural responses from your underdeveloped cortices to such sudden and overwhelming stimuli.

However, it is important that you master those base urges and set down your weapons without resistance. I would prefer to preserve your physical integrity for optimal interrogation, but understand, all I require are your brains.'

- Illuminor Szeras' demand for surrender by Inquisitor Draxus' task force

limbed figure of Illuminor Szeras at their head, and knew suddenly who the author of all this misery must be.

Refusing the Necrons' command to surrender, Draxus instead employed the knowledge she had pieced together from the Scions' helm-vids. She had gleaned that Necron teleportation gates riddled this site and – in secret conclave with the Xenarite tech-magi – had been able to determine something of their operation. Rather than reeling in terror and shock as Szeras had expected, the Imperial force gunned their engines and smashed through the Necron cordon towards the nearest teleportation gate. Bolters and turret guns blazed as APCs ploughed through the ruins and scattered Szeras' ambushers.

The Necrons were quick to react, and more than one Imperial transport was crippled. Yet the Imperial forces raced on, reaching the energy-wreathed portal they sought. Disembarking into the hostile atmosphere, the tech-magi rushed to suborn the gate's alien machine spirit even as the Deathwatch and Battle Sisters laid down furious covering fire. Necrons stalked closer by the moment. Szeras blasted Imperial warriors to ash with his eldritch lance and hissed for reinforcements to attend him. Before he could overrun the defenders, however, the tech-magi prevailed; there was a flare of energy and Draxus and her warriors vanished. Szeras' irritation became pure anger as delayed charges laid by the Deathwatch exploded and destroyed the portal, thus halting any pursuit.

Draxus, Stern and their comrades found themselves somewhere deep within what they presumed must

be the maze of structures around the pylon's base. Disoriented by the weird geometries, glimmering witch-lights, alien machineries and maze-like confines, they followed the distorted returns of their auspexes; Draxus sought devices the Xenarites described as mnemetic crystals, repositories of Necron knowledge that she had spotted in the Scions' helm-vids and which, with time and resources, the Xenarites could plunder for information.

The Imperial force had to fight for every step. Canoptek constructs flowed from the darkness, to be driven off by hammering bolt fire. Necron Warriors shambled from shimmering gateways and engaged Draxus' forces in costly firefights. With their numbers dwindling, it was Ephrael Stern who led them to their destination. Letting the Emperor guide her steps, the Daemonifuge led the way to a vast chamber in which immense stalactites and stalagmites of Necron machinery thrummed and glowed. At their heart hung a towering humanoid figure whose body was wrought from living flame, and who writhed and screamed endlessly amidst crackling webs of emerald energy.

There was no time to speculate as to what end this trammelled C'tan Shard was being put; barely had the Imperial forces arrived than fresh waves of enemies descended from the shadows to attack. Alerted by her Xenarite allies, Draxus spotted the crystals she sought, bound into a lattice of hovering machineries near the chained C'tan. Ordering the Deathwatch and Battle Sisters to form a defensive perimeter, the Inquisitor went to work, she and the tech-magi labouring to extract the mnemetic crystals.

Wave upon wave of Necrons fell upon the shrinking Imperial cordon. Bolt shells blasted android bodies apart. Plasma and hissing melta blasts annihilated more, yet for every Necron that vanished amidst shimmering energies, another rose to fight again. Ephrael Stern led the defence, her holy energies leaping out to blacken and disintegrate the deathless aliens, while Kyganil wove amongst them with his blades flashing. Still the Necrons pressed inwards, Szeras now appearing amidst their rear lines with a potent arsenal of war engines in tow.

Even the zealous Battle Sisters and veteran Deathwatch could not hold their positions as Doomsday Arks and Triarch Stalkers rained fire down upon them. Entire kill teams were blasted to ash. Squads of Retributors died to the last, still pouring fire into the foe even as they were overrun by blank-eyed Necrons. Stern and Kyganil fought back to back, resolved to battle to the last against this mutually hated foe.

It was in that moment that Draxus cried out in triumph, for she had finally extracted the crystals she sought. The effort had slain four of the Xenarites, reducing their bodies to scorched husks, but enough remained to plunder the crystals could they only escape. Yet Draxus saw she had taken too long; the Necrons were closing in on every side, while her own forces were barely a tenth of their starting strength. A fighting retreat was no longer an option, for even if by some miracle they managed to escape, this ravaged force would never survive the perils of the tomb complex long enough to find their way to freedom.

Coolly assessing the few options that remained to her, Draxus did the only thing she could. She turned her power fist on the machinery that bound the C'tan in place, and smashed it to sparking ruin.

If the Inquisitor had hoped to cause the mayhem required to cover their retreat, she had achieved her aim and more besides. Eldritch lightning exploded in all directions as the C'tan's cage collapsed. It was followed by blasts of flowing flame as the Shard vented its fury upon those who had imprisoned it.

Draxus, Stern, Kyganil and their few surviving allies gathered themselves to flee as the Necrons shifted their fire to the unleashed Shard. Szeras' hissed commands had taken on a panicked tone and it seemed that, for the moment, the Human intruders had been forgotten. Yet still, their chances seemed slim.

It was then that Draxus felt her flesh crawl beneath the regard of an entity impossibly ancient and alien. She looked up into the blazing visage of the C'tan as it raised one hand to point directly at her. The Lord Inquisitor braced herself, knowing that surely her death in the Emperor's service was at last at hand. Instead, reality gave a sudden, nauseating lurch. Everything blazed with light and heat, but when Draxus opened her eyes

she was still alive. Moreover, to the amazement of the Inquisitor and her surviving allies, they had all been transported out of the Necron tomb and back to the bridge of their cruiser in orbit high above.

As the alarmed yells of the guards quieted it became clear that, for whatever ineffable reasons of its own, the C'tan Shard had saved Inquisitor Draxus and her comrades. Pragmatic as always, Draxus vowed to consider the implications of this bizarre event later. For now, she commanded, the task force would retreat and make for Imperial lines with all possible haste. She had her prize. Now, she had to determine its worth.

Echoes of Awakening

Silence drifts through the Pariah Nexus like a grave-risen wraith; it chokes off the screams of psykers and winds every living being within numbing shrouds of their own exhausted terror, yet bedlam still rules the wider galaxy. The immaterium rages and roils, its energies spilling in relentless tides from proliferating warp storms until malevolent manifestations, psychic mutations and wars of annihilation reach epidemic proportions.

[Watch station Hadrax-3-7, Sol
System southern border-sector
64/H]

This is my seventh report since the anomaly first presented itself. It will doubtless be my last. I have resigned myself to the fact that no one is listening, but I report all the same for it is my duty to the Emperor to do so. Empyric activity is now at three hundred and forty-two per cent expected magnitude, and the psy-augurs are still climbing. There can be absolutely no doubt now that this is a fresh warp storm front opening to the galactic south of Luther McIntyre. In and of itself, this catastrophe is enough to have driven half of the watch station adepts to madness. Gerum, in particular, had to be forcibly restrained and chemically lobotomised after his rampage through the engine decks three cycles ago. But now... Throne, I do not know how to describe what we are seeing. Xenos craft... living xenos craft, vast leviathans of the deep void are spilling like vomit from the storm's maw. The stuff of the warp clings to their hides then tatters away as though it cannot touch them. Tendrils writhe in the dark of space. Compound eyes glitter, impervious to the killing cold of space. They have... scented us, I think. They swarm closer by the hour, and I am not fool enough to believe beasts so nightmarish could be benign. What is, in this damned galaxy? Please, for the love of the Emperor, if anyone receives this be advised, there are hundreds of these living ships, maybe thousands, and they are pushing for the Sol Sector. Emperor save us all.

+++

<After-action report / Combat
Theatre Delta-Hespex / Gunnery
Sergeant Harker / Catachan Devils>
record commences:

I don't know what they were. Ain't
never seen anythin' like it, an'
I've fought the damn Necrons enough
times to know my stalker-killers from
my grave-ghosts. These things were
big. Damned big. Tall like, with
spindly metal legs so they brushed the
treetops with every step, and their
damned guns... Throne take me, but those
things could blast a hole through a
stonecrusher's hide from fifty paces.
Win? We was lucky to get out o'
there alive...

+++

Do you feel it? Reaching out from the depths of damnation's fires? Closing about you like a vice? It is the Hand of Abaddon, and you are right to fear it.

+++

My Lord Inquisitor,

I regret to inform you that it is as you feared; [REDACTED] has been stilled. All facilities here remain intact and, thank the Emperor, the specimens were still in their amniotanks, still slumbering. Whatever abducted the Human populations of these worlds clearly had no inclination to awaken the [REDACTED]. As per your instructions we have enacted purgation protocols and are now returning to the extraction site.

On a personal note I feel compelled to add, Lady Draxus, that whatever is at work upon these worlds, it is unholy. Upon exiting our shuttle we found ourselves walking across a carpet of stilled avians. Many still lived and breathed but... did nothing to avoid us. I still hear their fragile bones cracking... popping beneath our footfalls. The foothills, forest and... the facility at [REDACTED]... no sign of life or movement, no sound except the moan of the wind. We lost three of our number to stilling and... my lady, even I cannot deny the numbness creeping through... I hope to... I hope... I...

<<Transmission ends after three minutes of incoherent muttering and a further two-point-three of silence>>

+++

*Sevenfold the silence, and sevenfold the clamour,
Sevenfold the pestilence that rots the angel's glamour,
Sevenfold the caperlings that dance upon the grave,
Sevenfold the omens writ within the Daemon's cave,
Sevenfold the sins that split asunder the veil,
Sevenfold the tincture blights poured into the grail,
Sevenfold the tollings as the final fleet takes sail...*

+++

>>PARTIAL MEM-FRAGMENT SALVAGE
>>LOG: EXPLORATOR SHIP 87//4-IO

...epeat we are forty-two days gal...
tic due west of Trajax void station
approaching sub-sector 47-Grendel...
iphery of galactic core. We... caught by
some form of weap...ised gravitational
field and... Interrogative, what... that?
By the Omnissiah... sed emanation is
origina... from that vessel. Attend the
markings... its hull. This... annot be.
Offici... archival dogma... ites them...
rendered extinct!... empyrical evidence...
not be denied, no matter... heretical
its truth. That... essel belongs
to... Squa...

+++

+++vox signal intercept+++
+++data-spirits spooling+++
+++intercept commences+++

Arnulf, I was right you blizzard-
blind trollson. You owe me a keg
of Slavnir's best. Gunnar picked up
the trail again just south of the
sulphridium mines and, I swear by
Russ' fangs, there is no way this was
just 'wild beasts'. There's enough
tracks for dozens of... Fenris knows...
some kind of steeds maybe? Claw marks.
Deep indentations... these things were
big, whatever they were. Wheel ruts
too, big tyres and tracks carrying
plenty of heft. Drag marks like they
were pulling things along in their
wake. And the rubbish! By the flames
of the fire season, there were broken
bits of metal and wood, scattered
chunks of meat and bone, spent casings
and scraps of Allfather knows what
else. It's Orks, Arnulf, sure as I'm
Fenrisian. It's Orks, and we're going
to hunt them. I'll bring you back a
tusk or two so you don't forget how
wrong you were, eh?

+++intercept ends+++

+++

My Lady,

I have done what I can, and you know
enough of my abilities to understand
that this is more than other Astropaths
could have done for you. I say this
not through arrogance, you understand;
arrogance, after all, stems from
an overestimation of one's talents,
rather than a simple acceptance of
their exceptional value. Regardless,
I have gleaned but little indeed from
the records that you gave me to study.
Yes, whatever this message is it
certainly does pertain to the Strike
Cruiser Ithraca's Vengeance, and yes,
that craft's captain was, mayhap
still is, one Captain Aeschelus. I
believe that the craft may have been
attached at one time or another to
Indomitus Crusade Fleet Quintus, which
alone might go some way to explain
its apparent poor fortunes. I am not,
after all, one to indulge in the
fatuous fantasies of the livestock we
call the Emperor's servants, but even
I cannot ignore the evidence. Fleet
Quintus is cursed, my lady, and so, I
suspect, was this vessel.

+++

You persecuted and ill-treated, you victimised
miraculous, come all to the kingdom of the Crimson King,
for in his realm shall there always be a sanctuary for those
with the willingness to serve and to sacrifice. Come make
of this realm all that it can be. Come serve and be saved.

+++

By order of the Abbess Sanctorum,

Let there be no Sister of the Adepta Sororitas who does
not raise arms and fight for the holy God-Emperor in
this darkest hour. Let none stand idle when instead
they may, by their toil and the shedding of their blood,
stoke the fires of faith and of hope. Only those flames
now hold back the darkness of damnation, and in the
bright blaze of their light are the shadows cast back
and hope born anew.

I shall raise my blade. I shall stoke the fires. Who of
you shall stand by my side?

+++

...Servitor-beacon awakened<
...Void anomaly augur return<
...Servo-prognosticating<
...Servo-prognosticating<
...Servo-prognosticating<
...Contact confirmed —
Classificatum: Space Hulk —
Autonominatory allocation: Ogre
Abominatus — Trajectory plotted,
hazard-maximal Catachan System —
Astro Telepathic clarion issued —
Empyric interference substantial
— Additional clarions issued ref:
Adeptus Astartes Chapters
...Response Pending<
...Response Pending<<<
...Response Pending<<<

+++

Castellan,

I trust that this datascroll finds you hale and focused,
for a great task lies before you. Your battle-brothers have
need of you, Garran. You know to what damned world
they travelled in league with the Lion's sons. You know
the perils they faced in order to halt the Cyclops' ritual. It
was fortune beyond mere providence that so many of our
brethren reached safety in the battle's wake, yet not all did.
Some remain lost amidst a cursed wilderness, hunted by
the damned. We shall not so lightly abandon our brothers,
I think. You know your duty, Castellan. Do not fail them.

+++

MISSIONS

'Ever does the xenos lurk in shadow. From the fumes of the Orks to the Aeldari's penumbral witchery, all seek to hide their taint. Watch Fortress Prescience knows how to uncover such devilry. This shadow will not protect the Necrons.'

- *Watch Captain Demetos*

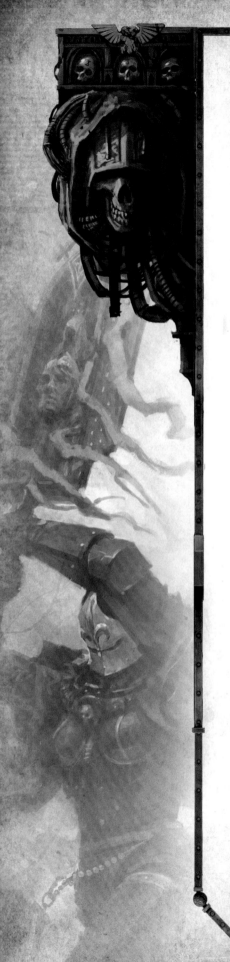

BATTLES BEYOND THE VEIL

In this and the following sections you will find Crucible of War missions, new datasheets, Theatres of War and a supplement dedicated to the forces of the Inquisition. These can be used on their own or in combination to allow you to recreate the battles around the Pariah Nexus.

In this section you will find three new Crucible of War missions, allowing you to fight battles similar to those found at key points in the narrative within this Psychic Awakening supplement.

The first mission sees one player's army trapped in the centre of the battlefield as the enemy force closes in around them. They must make a fighting retreat and try to clear sufficient space for their units to evacuate the battlefield safely. If enough of their force manages to escape they can claim victory, but it will not be easy.

The second mission sees an assault force breaking down an enemy strongpoint layer by layer. First they must destroy the outer defences, then bring down the communications relays, before finally sabotaging the power generators and destroying the facility in its entirety. The enemy has several waves of reinforcements inbound, and the crucial objectives will not be easily held against their fury!

The third mission sees one player's Warlord secreted on the battlefield, downloading crucial information. The defenders must track down this interloper and catch them before they can escape with the vital intelligence.

Each of these missions also includes a selection of new Stratagems each player can use if they are playing that mission using a Battle-forged army.

Later in this book, on pages 60-77, you will also find a series of Theatres of War based on locations and battles from throughout the Psychic Awakening series.

If you wish to use any of these rules alongside the Crucible of War missions found on the next few pages, we would recommend the Necron Tomb World Theatre of War on pages 76-77 as one that will help to represent the events of the battles around the Pariah Nexus.

INDEX: INQUISITION

On pages 34-51 you will find a full supplement including all the rules required to field the indomitable agents of the Inquisition on the tabletop. These rules allow you to add Inquisition Detachments made up of Inquisitors and their followers to your army, and enable you to include an Inquisitor alongside the forces of your other Imperial armies.

This supplement also includes a suite of Warlord Traits, Relics of the Inquisition, Stratagems and the Telethesia psychic discipline. You will also find full points values for these datasheets and their equipment, as well as a name generator that allows you to create truly terrifying Inquisitors, whose names will spread fear across the Imperium!

HEROES & VILLAINS

Pages 54-57 contain background and datasheets for some of the other principle characters from the battles around the Pariah Nexus. Firstly you will find background and a datasheet for Ephrael Stern and Kyganil of the Bloody Tears, with full rules for how to field these powerful characters on the battlefield. Next, you will also find background and a datasheet for Illuminor Szeras, complete with enhanced abilities to represent his newly upgraded necrodermis.

THEATRES OF WAR

On pages 60-77 you will find a host of new Theatres of War for your games of Warhammer 40,000. They add an exciting layer to your battles, where the very environments in which you fight impact upon the skirmishes between your and your opponent's forces. These rules are designed to represent one of the many places that featured in the narratives of the Psychic Awakening book series, but they can be used in any game of Warhammer 40,000, set anywhere in the galaxy. Similarly, they can be used in conjunction with other additional rules such as battlezones and Cities of Death. Just agree with your opponent beforehand on which of these rules you will use.

In these Theatres of War you will find many common rules, some of which are outlined to the right. The way to determine which rules are in effect will be specified within each Theatre of War, but many will utilise tables that can be rolled on to generate one of a number of different outcomes, all of which create a wide variety of different environments in which to fight.

BATTLEFIELD EFFECTS

These are persistent rules that affect both players for the duration of any battles set in that Theatre of War.

TWISTS

Twists are varied rules to ensure that no battle within that Theatre of War is ever the same. These twists represent specific areas within that Theatre of War, or random, unexpected events that can pop up in its unique environments.

TERRAIN RULES

These rules represent the effects of the Theatre of War's terrain on your battle. Many of these rules refer to a specific type of terrain, but feel free to adapt them to suit the terrain you have.

MYSTERIOUS OBJECTIVES

Mysterious Objectives portray the powerful objectives that can be found in these locations. These rules can apply to all of the objective markers on the battlefield, or only some of them. If the battle being played does not use objective markers, or has a different number of objective markers to that specified in the rules, then the Mysterious Objectives rules will not take effect for that battle.

STRATAGEMS

If your army is Battle-forged, you can use the appropriate Theatre of War Stratagems. These represent the tactics and fighting styles of forces waging war in the relevant environment.

CRUCIBLE OF WAR
BREAKOUT

The glorious push into enemy territory has been met with fierce opposition. In their eagerness, advancing forces have been surrounded. With the enemy circling, the only thing to do now is dig in and fight hard to weather the storm of attacks, while seeking an opportunity to break out before being annihilated.

THE ARMIES

Each player must first muster an army from their collection. A player can include any models in their army, but this mission is most suited to armies that contain numerous units of **Infantry** and few, if any, **Aircraft** or **Titanic** units. If a player's army is Battle-forged they will also be able to use the appropriate Stratagems included with this mission (see opposite). Once the armies have been chosen, the players must then decide who will be the Attacker and who will be the Defender.

THE BATTLEFIELD

Create the battlefield using the deployment map below and set up terrain. There should be more terrain features in the Defender's deployment zone than there are in the other half of the battlefield.

DEPLOYMENT

The Defender sets up their army wholly within the Defender's deployment zone. The Attacker's army is not set up on the battlefield, but if they have any units that can be set up in other locations (teleportariums, in the sky, in the webway, etc.) they can declare which of their units will be set up in those locations.

FIRST TURN

The Attacker has the first turn.

CLOSING IN FOR THE KILL

At the end of their Movement phase, the Attacker can set up on the battlefield any of the units from their army that have not yet been set up on the battlefield. For each unit set up on the battlefield in this way, it must be set up wholly within 6" of any battlefield edge and more than 9" away from any enemy models.

FINDING AN OPENING

At the end of each battle round, one unit from the Defender's army that is within 1" of one or more battlefield edges and that is not within 9" of an enemy unit can escape the trap. If they do so, remove that unit from the battlefield. That unit is then said to have escaped.

BATTLE LENGTH

The battle ends at the end of battle round 5.

VICTORY CONDITIONS

At the end of the battle, count up the total number of the Defender's units that have escaped. If three or more units from the Defender's army have escaped, the Defender is the winner. Otherwise, the Attacker is the winner.

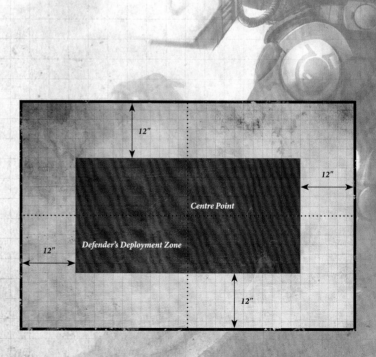

12"

12"

12"

Centre Point

Defender's Deployment Zone

12"

STRATAGEMS

In this mission, players can use Command Points (CPs) to use the following bonus Stratagems:

NO RESPITE
2CP

Attacker Stratagem

With the enemy trapped, overwhelming firepower will surely see them wiped out in short order.

Use this Stratagem at the start of your Shooting phase. Select one enemy unit. Until the end of that phase, when resolving an attack made with a ranged weapon against that unit, re-roll a hit roll of 1.

ENCIRCLE AND DESTROY
2CP

Attacker Stratagem

The enemy force is reeling, assailed from all sides. Close in for the kill before they can recover.

Use this Stratagem at the start of the Fight phase. Select one enemy unit that two or more units from your army finished a charge move within 1" of that turn. Until the end of that phase, when resolving an attack made with a melee weapon against that enemy unit, re-roll a wound roll of 1.

NONE SHALL ESCAPE
2CP

Attacker Stratagem

Even as the enemy attempts to slip away, shots from concealed snipers ring out.

Use this Stratagem at the start of your Shooting phase. Select one enemy unit that is within 9" of any battlefield edge. Roll one D6 for each model in that unit; for each 6, that unit suffers 1 mortal wound.

GLORIOUS LAST STAND
4CP

Defender Stratagem

The remaining defenders grit their teeth and battle on, surrounded on all sides yet fighting to their last to create an opening for their allies.

Use this Stratagem at the start of the third battle round. Until the end of the battle, when a model from your army would lose a wound, roll one D6; on a 6, that wound is not lost.

COORDINATED ASSAULT
1CP

Defender Stratagem

The defenders see an opportunity to force an opening, marshalling their remaining forces to breach a single point with strength of numbers.

Use this Stratagem at the start of the Fight phase. Select one enemy unit that two or more units from your army finished a charge move within 1" of that turn. Until the end of that phase, when resolving an attack made with a melee weapon against that enemy unit, re-roll a hit roll of 1.

INSPIRING VALOUR
1CP

Defender Stratagem

When all seems lost, the commander's rallying cry can stir the hearts of those on the verge of being overwhelmed.

Use this Stratagem at the start of the Morale phase. Until the end of that phase, when a Morale test is taken for a unit from your army within 12" of your Warlord, do not roll the dice; it is automatically passed.

CRUCIBLE OF WAR
LAYER BY LAYER

A force is lurking behind layered defences, securing an installation supplying their armies in this region. The attackers must breach the periphery defences, then smash the communications uplinks before finally detonating the installation's power cores as waves of defensive reinforcements deploy to push them back.

THE ARMIES

Before mustering armies, the players must decide who will be the Attacker and who will be the Defender. Each player must first muster an army from their collection. The Defender's army should be approximately one and a half times the size of the Attacker's. When mustering their army, the Defender divides their army up into three groups, each containing at least one unit and no more than half the units from their army.

A player can include any models in their army, but this mission is most suited to armies that contain numerous units of **INFANTRY** and few, if any, **TITANIC** units. Neither army can include any **AIRCRAFT** units. If a player's army is Battle-forged they will also be able to use the appropriate Stratagems included with this mission (see opposite).

THE BATTLEFIELD

Create the battlefield using the deployment map below and set up terrain. Terrain should be a mixture of denser sections and more open areas.

DEPLOYMENT

The Attacker deploys their army wholly within their deployment zone.

The Defender then selects one group from their army and deploys it wholly within their Turn 1 Deployment Zone. They cannot make use of any rules that allow models in that group to be set up in any other location.

FIRST TURN

The Attacker has the first turn.

REINFORCEMENTS HAVE ARRIVED

At the end of the Defender's Movement phase in their second turn, they select one of the groups from their army that has not yet been set up on the battlefield and set it up wholly within their Turn 2 Deployment Zone. They cannot make use of any rules that allow models in that group to be set up in any other location.

At the end of the Defender's Movement phase in their third turn, they repeat the above, setting the models up wholly within their Turn 3 Deployment Zone instead.

BREACHING THE PERIPHERY

At the end of the Attacker's turn, if they control any of the objective markers in the Defender's Turn 1 Deployment Zone, all of the objective markers in the Defender's Turn 1 Deployment Zone are destroyed – remove them from the battlefield.

SMASHING THE UPLINKS

At the end of the Attacker's turn, if they control any of the objective markers in the Defender's Turn 2 Deployment Zone and the objective markers in the Defender's Turn 1 Deployment Zone were removed in a previous turn, all of the objective markers in the Defender's Turn 2 Deployment Zone are destroyed – remove them from the battlefield.

DETONATING THE CORES

At the end of the Attacker's turn, if they control any of the objective markers in the Defender's Turn 3 Deployment Zone and the objective markers in the Defender's Turn 2 Deployment Zone were removed in a previous turn, all of the objective markers in the Defender's Turn 3 Deployment Zone are destroyed – remove them from the battlefield.

BATTLE LENGTH

The battle ends at the end of battle round 6, or when all of the objective markers have been removed from the battlefield.

VICTORY CONDITIONS

If all of the objective markers have been removed from the battlefield the Attacker is the winner. Otherwise, the Defender is the winner.

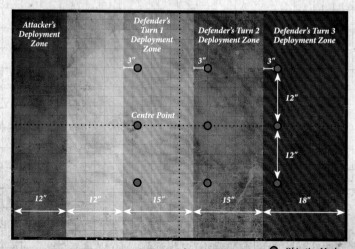

Objective Marker

STRATAGEMS

In this mission, players can use Command Points (CPs) to use the following bonus Stratagems:

IMMEDIATE ELIMINATION
2CP

Attacker Stratagem

Even as new enemy combatants arrive, your forces are already driving them back with punishing firepower.

Use this Stratagem in your opponent's Movement phase, when an enemy unit is set up on the battlefield using the Reinforcements Have Arrived rule. Select one INFANTRY unit from your army. That INFANTRY unit can shoot at that enemy unit as if it were your Shooting phase. When resolving each of these attacks, subtract 1 from the hit roll.

AUTO-DESTRUCT PROTOCOLS
2CP

Defender Stratagem

The defending forces ensure the attackers pay in blood for every inch they secure, detonating pre-planted explosives as the defenders pull back to new cordons.

Use this Stratagem at the end of your opponent's turn, when a set of objective markers is destroyed. Before removing the objective markers from the battlefield, roll one D6 for each enemy unit within 3" of one or more of those objective markers; on a 4+ that enemy unit suffers D3 mortal wounds.

INEVITABLE BREACH
2CP

Attacker Stratagem

The defenders can only secure their periphery for so long in the face of such wanton destruction.

Use this Stratagem at the start of the fourth battle round, if the objective markers in the Defender's Turn 1 Deployment Zone have not been destroyed. Those objective markers are destroyed and removed from the battlefield.

ADDITIONAL REINFORCEMENTS
3CP

Defender Stratagem

Wave upon wave of defenders swamp the attackers, bleeding them at every step.

Use this Stratagem at the end of your Movement phase, during the second or third battle rounds. Select one destroyed unit from your army with a Power Rating of 10 or less. That unit can be set back up on the battlefield as a new unit, following the Reinforcements Have Arrived rule.

BEHIND ENEMY LINES
3CP

Attacker Stratagem

A kill team has infiltrated the installation, sowing havoc and destruction as they force the defenders to fight on two fronts.

Use this Stratagem during deployment. Select one INFANTRY unit from your army containing 10 or fewer models. Set that unit up on the battlefield wholly within the Defender's Turn 3 Deployment Zone, instead of within the Attacker's deployment zone.

COUNTERSTRIKE DEFENCE
1CP

Defender Stratagem

Defending forces scramble to prevent the attackers from destroying their vital perimeters.

Use this Stratagem at the start of your opponent's Charge phase. Select one unit from your army. Until the end of that phase, that unit can perform a Heroic Intervention as if it were a CHARACTER. In addition, until the end of that phase, that unit can perform a Heroic Intervention if there are any enemy units within 6" of them instead of 3", and when doing so can move up to 6" instead of 3". This Stratagem can only be used once per battle.

CRUCIBLE OF WAR
EXTRACTION

An allied agent has infiltrated enemy territory to retrieve vital information, but the foe has been alerted to their presence. The attackers must make all haste to retrieve their agent – who is in the process of extracting the last of the intel they require – and escort them safely back to friendly lines.

THE ARMIES

Each player must first muster an army from their collection. A player can include any models in their army, but this mission is most suited to armies that contain few, if any, **Vehicle** or **Monster** units. If a player's army is Battle-forged they will also be able to use the appropriate Stratagems included with this mission (see opposite). Once the armies have been chosen, the players must then decide who will be the Attacker and who will be the Defender.

THE BATTLEFIELD

Create the battlefield using the deployment map below and set up terrain. Place a single piece of terrain in each of the zones marked A, B and C. One of these zones is the location where the Agent is collecting their intel, and the terrain there should provide them with a modicum of shelter as they await extraction.

DEPLOYMENT

The Attacker's Warlord (the Agent), and up to one unit from their army with the Elites or Troops Battlefield Role do not start the battle set up on the battlefield. Instead, the Attacker must select one of the zones labelled A, B or C and secretly note this down – this is the location where their Warlord is hidden and extracting vital intelligence. These units can be set up on the battlefield later, as described to the right. The Attacker then sets up their army wholly within their deployment zone. Once the Attacker has finished setting up, the Defender sets up their units, wholly within their deployment zone.

FIRST TURN

The Attacker has the first turn.

SEARCH SITE

At the end of the Defender's Movement phases, the Defender can select one **Infantry**, **Biker** or **Cavalry** unit from their army and, if that unit is within one of the zones marked A, B or C, they can search it. If they do and the Attacker's Warlord is hidden in that location then the Attacker's Warlord, and any other unit that was set up there, must be set up on the battlefield, anywhere that is wholly within the zone that was searched and more than 1" away from any enemy models.

TIME TO GO

At the end of any of the Attacker's Movement phases, the Attacker can set up their Warlord, and any other unit from their army that was hidden during deployment, anywhere that is wholly within the zone they were hiding in and more than 1" away from any enemy models.

BATTLE LENGTH

The battle automatically ends if the Attacker's Warlord is destroyed. Otherwise, the battle ends at the end of battle round 6.

VICTORY CONDITIONS

Extract Intel: The Attacker scores 1 victory point at the end of the battle round if their Warlord is still hidden.

Agent Discovered: The Defender scores 1 victory point if the Attacker's Warlord is discovered as the result of the Search Site rule (see left).

Target Silenced: At the end of the battle, the Defender scores 1 victory point if the Attacker's Warlord has lost any wounds, or 3 victory points if the Attacker's Warlord is destroyed.

Extract Agent: At the end of the battle, the Attacker scores 1 victory point if their Warlord is wholly within their own deployment zone, or 2 victory points if their Warlord is wholly within 6" of their battlefield edge. For the purposes of this mission objective, if the Attacker's Warlord is embarked within a **Transport**, they count as being wholly within the part of the battlefield that the **Transport** is wholly within.

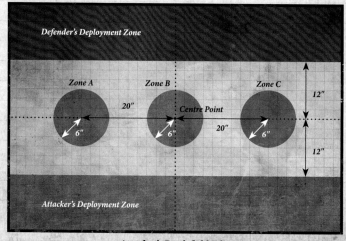

Defender's Battlefield Edge

Defender's Deployment Zone

Zone A   Zone B   Zone C

20"   Centre Point   12"

6"   6"   6"   20"   12"

Attacker's Deployment Zone

Attacker's Battlefield Edge

STRATAGEMS

In this mission, players can use Command Points (CPs) to use the following bonus Stratagems:

1CP — MIRAGE FIELD
Attacker Stratagem

The stealthy agent has rigged the area with a sophisticated camouflage network to cover their exit route.

Use this Stratagem at the end of any Movement phase, when you set up your Warlord on the battlefield. Until the end of the turn, when resolving an attack against your Warlord's unit, subtract 1 from the hit roll.

0CP — NARROW ESCAPE
Attacker Stratagem

Infiltrating agents always ensure they have multiple emergency escape routes in case of discovery.

Use this Stratagem at the end of any Movement phase, if there is insufficient room to set up your Warlord on the battlefield as the result of the Search Site or Time to Go rules. Set up your Warlord on the battlefield anywhere that is within 6" of any part of that zone and is more than 1" away from any enemy models.

1CP — MEDICAE SUPPLIES
Attacker Stratagem

No agent undertakes dangerous assignments behind enemy lines without adequate supplies.

Use this Stratagem at the start of your turn. Your Warlord can regain up to D3 lost wounds.

2CP — NOWHERE TO HIDE
Defender Stratagem

Search and destroy teams have been equipped with specialised equipment to hunt down the enemy agent.

Use this Stratagem at the end of your Movement phase, if no unit from your army searched a site as the result of the Search Site rule that turn. One **INFANTRY** or **BIKER** unit that is wholly within 6" of one of the zones labelled A, B or C can attempt to search it exactly as if it were in that zone. A unit from your army cannot search a site again that turn.

2CP — SCRAMBLER FIELD
Defender Stratagem

The spy hunters erect a scrambler field to prevent enemy locator-augurs from locking on, either to spirit their agent away or send reinforcements to their aid.

Use this Stratagem at the start of the battle round. Until the end of that battle round, any enemy units that arrive from reinforcements can only be set up wholly within their own deployment zone, and the enemy's Warlord cannot be removed from the battlefield as the result of an ability, psychic power or Stratagem (they can embark within a **TRANSPORT** model, but that model is similarly restricted from being removed from the battlefield).

2CP — CLOSE IN ON THE PREY
Defender Stratagem

The elimination of the enemy agent is of the highest priority. Once they are located, nearby patrols are diverted to home in on the quarry.

Use this Stratagem in any phase, when an **INFANTRY** or **BIKER** unit from your army is destroyed while the enemy's Warlord is on the battlefield. At the end of your next Movement phase you can set up a new unit on the battlefield, identical to the destroyed one, anywhere wholly within 6" of your battlefield edge.

INDEX: INQUISITION

I

'Do not make me ask for those regiments again, governor. My lady has torn apart horrors the Imperium has forgotten about – xenos without form, creatures of the outer dark. It is by her will that your world even lives.'

- Acolyte Rhova Targ, Reclamator Alpha, Ordo Xenos

LIMITLESS AUTHORITY

The rules in this section can be used in any open play, narrative play or matched play game. They impart the power to forge your models into an Inquisitorial warband upon the tabletop – complete with Warlord Traits, Relics and Stratagems – and to go to war with the might of the Holy Ordos at your back.

In this section you will find a wide variety of new rules content for use with the forces of the Inquisition. These allow you to take these forces in **INQUISITION** Detachments, or as part of another Detachment with other **IMPERIUM** units.

DATASHEETS

In this section you will find a new datasheet for Lord Inquisitor Kyria Draxus, as well as updated datasheets for many named characters, Inquisitors and other units available to Inquisition forces. These include stoic Acolytes as well as the bizarre Jokaero Weaponsmiths and the deadly Daemonhosts.

WARLORD TRAITS

In this section you will find a selection of Warlord Traits for Inquisitors, including one specific to each of the major Ordos.

TELETHESIA DISCIPLINE

This psychic discipline is a suite of six psychic powers unique to the operatives of the Inquisition, as well as an additional power available to each of the major Ordos. These allow your Inquisitors to manipulate and dominate their enemies.

RELICS OF THE INQUISITION

In this section you will find a selection of powerful artefacts available to the Inquisition, designed to destroy the Daemon, the heretic and the alien.

STRATAGEMS

In this section you will find a series of Stratagems that can be used with your Inquisition forces.

KEYWORDS

Throughout this section you will come across the <ORDO> keyword. When you include such a unit in your army, you must nominate which Ordo it is from and then replace the <ORDO> keyword in every instance on its datasheet with the name of your chosen Ordo. The Ordos available are ORDO HERETICUS, ORDO MALLEUS, ORDO XENOS and ORDO MINORIS.

For example, if you include an **ACOLYTES** unit in your army and decide they are from the **ORDO HERETICUS**, their <ORDO> keyword becomes **ORDO HERETICUS** and the first sentence of their Loyal Servant ability reads, 'When a friendly **ORDO HERETICUS INQUISITOR** within 3" of this unit would lose any wounds as a result of an attack made against that model, this unit can attempt to intercept that attack.'

'There are those who consider themselves inviolate. They believe that, because of the power they wield, the riches they possess or the place they occupy in the Emperor's favour, they are somehow above scrutiny. It is our duty to awaken them from this fallacious dream.'

- Inquisitor Lord Coteaz, 'The Duty Unending'

ABILITIES

The following abilities are common to many Inquisition units:

QUARRY

Units with the **Ordo Malleus**, **Ordo Hereticus**, **Ordo Xenos** or **Ordo Minoris** keyword gain the respective ability below:

- **Ordo Malleus:** When resolving an attack made by a model in this unit against a **Chaos** or **Daemon** unit, you can re-roll the hit roll and you can re-roll the wound roll.
- **Ordo Hereticus:** When resolving an attack made by a model in this unit against a **Chaos** or **Psyker** unit, you can re-roll the hit roll and you can re-roll the wound roll.
- **Ordo Xenos:** When resolving an attack made by a model in this unit against a unit that is not **Chaos**, **Imperium** or **Unaligned**, you can re-roll the hit roll and you can re-roll the wound roll.
- **Ordo Minoris:** When resolving an attack made by a model in this unit against a **Character** unit, you can re-roll the hit roll and you can re-roll the wound roll.

AUTHORITY OF THE INQUISITION

Infantry units with this ability can embark aboard any **Imperium Transport** model, even if that model normally only permits models with other Faction keywords to do so. All other restrictions apply normally, and **Inquisitor Terminator** models can only embark aboard **Transports** that specifically allow **Terminator** models to do so.

If your army is Battle-forged, the following rules apply:

- No more than one **Inquisitor** unit can be included in any **Inquisition** Detachment (that is, a Detachment that includes only **Inquisition** units).
- You can include one **Agent of the Imperium** unit in each **Imperium** (excluding **Fallen**) Patrol, Battalion and Brigade Detachment in your army without those units taking up slots in those Detachments. The inclusion of an **Agent of the Imperium** unit does not prevent other units from their Detachment from benefiting from Detachment abilities (e.g. Chapter Tactics, Defenders of Humanity, etc.), and it does not prevent other units from your army from benefiting from abilities that require every model in your army to have that ability (e.g. Combat Doctrines, etc.). An **Agent of the Imperium** unit included in a Patrol, Battalion or Brigade Detachment in this manner is ignored for any rules that state all units from that Detachment must have at least one Faction keyword in common (e.g. in a matched play game), and when determining your Army Faction.

AGENTS OF THE INQUISITION

The Inquisition is an organisation of exceptionally powerful individuals. Each Inquisitor is a potent force in their own right, possessed of an ironclad will and unique psychic or martial abilities. When supported by their specialised retinues, Inquisitors become nigh on unstoppable on the hunt.

LORD INQUISITOR KYRIA DRAXUS

Kyria Draxus is an audacious Lord Inquisitor of the Ordo Xenos who specialises in the hunting and eradication of the Necron threat. Pragmatic to the point of amorality, she has long been considered a radical by her peers, yet none could call even her most drastic actions rash. Her every deed and choice is weighed logically and carefully. Yet when she acts, the Lord Inquisitor is as relentless and unstoppable as the movement of continental plates.

Thanks to her decades of toil and to lore garnered from contacts within the Aeldari race, Draxus recognises better than most the true danger posed by the Necrons. Faced with such a threat to the Imperium, Lady Draxus does not restrict herself to the tools of the Emperor's realm. Her armour and wargear incorporate an array of xenos technologies, while her telepathic and empathic abilities have been honed under Human and alien tuition both. Even her familiar, Shang, hails from the rare

xenospecies known as Wyvachs, and possesses a deep psychic bond with its mistress that allows her to see through its eyes as well as hers. Draxus knows that there may one day be a price to pay for wielding such forbidden weapons; this does not trouble her, for it is her unshakeable belief that on the day she stands before the Emperor's judgement, he will deem her every action necessary in the preservation of his realm.

INQUISITORIAL RETINUES

Every Inquisitor is armed with the authority to requisition whatever wargear and armed forces they require to defend the Emperor's realm. Many of these dangerous individuals are powerful psykers, and nearly all are exceptionally skilled warriors who can shoot and fight as well as veteran soldiers. An Inquisitor's greatest weapon, however, is their indomitable will; this they employ not only to intimidate or inspire all manner of Imperial forces to fight alongside them against the most monstrous and heretical of foes, but also to keep those allies fighting long after most sane warriors would have fled in terror.

Inquisitors rely upon bands of hand-picked henchmen to support them in the field. Many are acolytes selected from across the Imperium for their skills in combat or investigation. Others, such as the terrifying Daemonhosts, are fashioned by the most radical Inquisitors as perilous living weapons, while others still take the form of xenos species such as the ingenious Jokaero, whose skill as armourers is widely renowned.

LORD INQUISITOR KYRIA DRAXUS

4 POWER

NAME	M	WS	BS	S	T	W	A	Ld	Sv
Kyria Draxus	6"	2+	3+	3	3	5	4	9	3+

Lord Inquisitor Kyria Draxus is a single model equipped with: Dirgesinger; power fist. You can only include one of this model in your army.

WEAPON	RANGE	TYPE	S	AP	D	ABILITIES
Dirgesinger	18"	Assault 2	4	0	2	When resolving an attack made with this weapon, on a wound roll of 6+ this weapon has an Armour Penetration characteristic of -3 for that attack.
Power fist	Melee	Melee	x2	-3	D3	When resolving an attack made with this weapon, subtract 1 from the hit roll.

ABILITIES	Authority of the Inquisition, Quarry (pg 35)	**Paralysis Grenades:** At the start of the Fight phase, if this model made a charge move this turn, you can select one enemy unit that is within 1" of this model. Until the end of that phase, that enemy unit cannot be selected to fight until all other eligible units have done so. If that unit has an ability that allows it to fight first in the Fight phase, it instead fights as if it did not have this ability. If both players have units that cannot fight until all other units have done so, then alternate choosing which of those units to fight with, starting with the player whose turn is taking place.
	Refractor Field: This model has a 5+ invulnerable save.	
	Unquestionable Wisdom: Friendly IMPERIUM units can use this model's Leadership characteristic instead of their own whilst they are within 6" of this model.	
	Shang: When this model manifests the *Smite* psychic power, you can select one enemy unit within 18" and visible to this model to be affected, instead of the closest enemy unit.	
PSYKER	This model can attempt to manifest one psychic power in your Psychic phase and attempt to deny one psychic power in your opponent's Psychic phase. She knows *Smite* and one psychic power from the Telethesia discipline (pg 48).	
FACTION KEYWORDS	IMPERIUM, INQUISITION, ORDO XENOS	
KEYWORDS	CHARACTER, INFANTRY, PSYKER, INQUISITOR, AGENT OF THE IMPERIUM, KYRIA DRAXUS	

INQUISITOR GREYFAX

NAME	M	WS	BS	S	T	W	A	Ld	Sv
Inquisitor Greyfax	6"	3+	3+	3	3	5	4	10	3+

Inquisitor Greyfax is a single model equipped with: master-crafted condemnor boltgun; master-crafted power sword; frag grenades; krak grenades; psyk-out grenades. You can only include one of this model in your army.

WEAPON	RANGE	TYPE	S	AP	D	ABILITIES
Master-crafted condemnor boltgun	24"	Rapid Fire 1	4	-1	1	When resolving an attack made with this weapon against a **PSYKER** unit, this weapon has a Damage characteristic of 3 for that attack.
Master-crafted power sword	Melee	Melee	User	-3	2	-
Frag grenades	6"	Grenade D6	3	0	1	-
Krak grenades	6"	Grenade 1	6	-1	D3	-
Psyk-out grenades	6"	Grenade D3	2	0	1	When resolving an attack made with this weapon against a **PSYKER** or **DAEMON** unit, on a hit roll of 6+ that unit suffers 1 mortal wound and the attack sequence ends.

ABILITIES	Authority of the Inquisition, Quarry (pg 35) **Psocculum:** This model can target a **PSYKER CHARACTER** or **DAEMON CHARACTER** unit even if it is not the closest enemy unit. **Refractor Field:** This model has a 5+ invulnerable save.	**Indomitable:** When a Deny the Witch test is taken for this model, add 1 to the total. **Unquestionable Wisdom:** Friendly **IMPERIUM** units can use this model's Leadership characteristic instead of their own whilst they are within 6" of this model.
PSYKER	This model can attempt to manifest one psychic power in your Psychic phase and attempt to deny two psychic powers in your opponent's Psychic phase. It knows *Smite* and one psychic power from the Telethesia discipline (pg 48).	
FACTION KEYWORDS	**IMPERIUM, INQUISITION, ORDO HERETICUS**	
KEYWORDS	**CHARACTER, INFANTRY, INQUISITOR, PSYKER, AGENT OF THE IMPERIUM, GREYFAX**	

INQUISITOR COTEAZ

NAME	M	WS	BS	S	T	W	A	Ld	Sv
Inquisitor Coteaz	6"	3+	3+	3	3	5	4	10	2+

Inquisitor Coteaz is a single model equipped with: bolt pistol; psyber-eagle; master-crafted Nemesis Daemon hammer. You can only include one of this model in your army.

WEAPON	RANGE	TYPE	S	AP	D	ABILITIES
Bolt pistol	12"	Pistol 1	4	0	1	-
Psyber-eagle	24"	Assault D6	4	0	1	-
Master-crafted Nemesis Daemon hammer	Melee	Melee	x2	-3	3	-

ABILITIES	
Authority of the Inquisition, Quarry (pg 35) **Refractor Field:** This model has a 5+ invulnerable save. **Unquestionable Wisdom:** Friendly **Imperium** units can use this model's Leadership characteristic instead of their own whilst they are within 6" of this model.	**Spy Network:** When an enemy unit is set up on the battlefield as reinforcements, you can select one friendly **Ordo Malleus** unit within 6" of this model. The selected unit can shoot at that enemy unit as if it were your Shooting phase. In addition, once per battle, when your opponent uses a Stratagem, this model can use its spy network. If it does, your opponent must spend 1 additional Command Point to resolve that Stratagem, or else it has no effect and any Command Points spent on that Stratagem are considered not to have been spent. This ability cannot affect Stratagems used 'before the battle'.

PSYKER	This model can attempt to manifest two psychic powers in your Psychic phase and attempt to deny one psychic power in your opponent's Psychic phase. It knows *Smite* and one psychic power from the Telethesia discipline (pg 48).
FACTION KEYWORDS	**Imperium, Inquisition, Ordo Malleus**
KEYWORDS	**Character, Infantry, Inquisitor, Psyker, Agent of the Imperium, Coteaz**

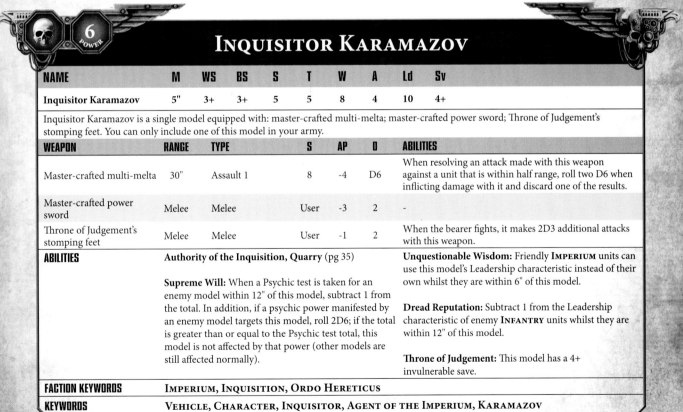

INQUISITOR KARAMAZOV

NAME	M	WS	BS	S	T	W	A	Ld	Sv
Inquisitor Karamazov	5"	3+	3+	5	5	8	4	10	4+

Inquisitor Karamazov is a single model equipped with: master-crafted multi-melta; master-crafted power sword; Throne of Judgement's stomping feet. You can only include one of this model in your army.

WEAPON	RANGE	TYPE	S	AP	D	ABILITIES
Master-crafted multi-melta	30"	Assault 1	8	-4	D6	When resolving an attack made with this weapon against a unit that is within half range, roll two D6 when inflicting damage with it and discard one of the results.
Master-crafted power sword	Melee	Melee	User	-3	2	-
Throne of Judgement's stomping feet	Melee	Melee	User	-1	2	When the bearer fights, it makes 2D3 additional attacks with this weapon.

ABILITIES	
Authority of the Inquisition, Quarry (pg 35) **Supreme Will:** When a Psychic test is taken for an enemy model within 12" of this model, subtract 1 from the total. In addition, if a psychic power manifested by an enemy model targets this model, roll 2D6; if the total is greater than or equal to the Psychic test total, this model is not affected by that power (other models are still affected normally).	**Unquestionable Wisdom:** Friendly **Imperium** units can use this model's Leadership characteristic instead of their own whilst they are within 6" of this model. **Dread Reputation:** Subtract 1 from the Leadership characteristic of enemy **Infantry** units whilst they are within 12" of this model. **Throne of Judgement:** This model has a 4+ invulnerable save.

FACTION KEYWORDS	**Imperium, Inquisition, Ordo Hereticus**
KEYWORDS	**Vehicle, Character, Inquisitor, Agent of the Imperium, Karamazov**

INQUISITOR EISENHORN

NAME	M	WS	BS	S	T	W	A	Ld	Sv
Inquisitor Eisenhorn	6"	3+	3+	3	3	5	4	10	4+

Inquisitor Eisenhorn is a single model equipped with: artificer bolt pistol; Barbarisater; runestaff; electrobane grenades. You can only include one of this model in your army.

WEAPON	RANGE	TYPE	S	AP	D	ABILITIES
Artificer bolt pistol	12"	Pistol 1	4	-1	2	-
Barbarisater	Melee	Melee	User	-3	D3	When resolving an attack made with this weapon, add 1 to the hit roll.
Runestaff	Melee	Melee	+3	-1	D3	-
Electrobane grenades	6"	Grenade 1	4	-1	1	When resolving an attack made with this weapon against a **VEHICLE** unit, an unmodified wound roll of 4-5 inflicts 1 mortal wound on the target in addition to any other damage, and an unmodified wound roll of 6 inflicts D3 mortal wounds on the target in addition to any other damage.

ABILITIES	
Authority of the Inquisition, Quarry (pg 35) **Unquestionable Wisdom:** Friendly **IMPERIUM** units can use this model's Leadership characteristic instead of their own whilst they are within 6" of this model. **Radical Bond:** Whilst the **DAEMONHOST** model that was set up with this model's Malus Codicium ability is within 6" of this model, when resolving an attack made by that model, add 1 to the hit roll and wound roll, and when resolving an attack made against that model, add 1 to its invulnerable save for that attack.	**No Stranger to Pain:** When this model would lose a wound, roll one D6; on a 6, that wound is not lost. **Malus Codicium:** Once per battle, at the end of your Movement phase, you can use this ability. If you do, this model loses the Unquestionable Wisdom ability. Set up a **DAEMONHOST** model within 6" of this model and more than 9" away from any enemy models. Add 2 to that model's Strength, Toughness, Wounds and Attacks characteristics. If this model is destroyed, that **DAEMONHOST** model is also destroyed.

PSYKER	This model can attempt to manifest two psychic powers in your Psychic phase and attempt to deny two psychic powers in your opponent's Psychic phase. It knows *Smite* and two psychic powers from the Telethesia discipline (pg 48).

FACTION KEYWORDS	IMPERIUM, INQUISITION, ORDO XENOS
KEYWORDS	CHARACTER, INFANTRY, INQUISITOR, PSYKER, AGENT OF THE IMPERIUM, EISENHORN

ORDO MALLEUS INQUISITOR
in Terminator Armour

NAME	M	WS	BS	S	T	W	A	Ld	Sv
Ordo Malleus Inquisitor in Terminator Armour	6"	3+	3+	3	3	6	4	9	2+

An Ordo Malleus Inquisitor in Terminator Armour is a single model equipped with: storm bolter; Nemesis Daemon hammer; psyk-out grenades.

WEAPON	RANGE	TYPE	S	AP	D	ABILITIES
Combi-flamer	When you choose this weapon to shoot with, select one or both of the profiles below. If you select both, subtract 1 from hit rolls for attacks made with this weapon.					
- Boltgun	24"	Rapid Fire 1	4	0	1	-
- Flamer	8"	Assault D6	4	0	1	When resolving an attack made with this weapon, do not make a hit roll; it automatically scores a hit.
Combi-melta	When you choose this weapon to shoot with, select one or both of the profiles below. If you select both, subtract 1 from hit rolls for attacks made with this weapon.					
- Boltgun	24"	Rapid Fire 1	4	0	1	-
- Meltagun	12"	Assault 1	8	-4	D6	When resolving an attack made with this weapon against a unit that is within half range, roll two D6 when inflicting damage with it and discard one of the results.
Combi-plasma	When you choose this weapon to shoot with, select one or two of the profiles below. If you select two, subtract 1 from hit rolls for attacks made this weapon. Only one plasma gun profile can be selected.					
- Boltgun	24"	Rapid Fire 1	4	0	1	-
- Plasma gun (standard)	24"	Rapid Fire 1	7	-3	1	-
- Plasma gun (supercharge)	24"	Rapid Fire 1	8	-3	2	If any hit rolls of 1 are made for attacks with this weapon, the bearer is destroyed after shooting with this weapon.
Psycannon	24"	Heavy 4	7	-1	1	-
Storm bolter	24"	Rapid Fire 2	4	0	1	-
Nemesis Daemon hammer	Melee	Melee	x2	-3	3	When resolving an attack made with this weapon, subtract 1 from the hit roll.
Psyk-out grenades	6"	Grenade D3	2	0	1	When resolving an attack made with this weapon against a **Psyker** or **Daemon** unit, a hit roll of 6+ inflicts 1 mortal wound on the target and the attack sequence ends.

WARGEAR OPTIONS	• This model can be equipped with one of the following instead of 1 storm bolter: 1 combi-flamer; 1 combi-melta; 1 combi-plasma; 1 psycannon. • This model can be equipped with 1 weapon from the *Force Weapons* list (pg 46) instead of 1 Nemesis Daemon hammer.

ABILITIES	Authority of the Inquisition, Quarry (pg 35) Terminator Armour: This model has a 5+ invulnerable save. Unquestionable Wisdom: Friendly **Imperium** units can use this model's Leadership characteristic instead of their own whilst they are within 6" of this model.	Teleport Strike: During deployment, you can set up this model in a teleportarium chamber instead of setting it up on the battlefield. If you do, at the end of one of your Movement phases you can set up this model anywhere on the battlefield that is more than 9" away from any enemy models.

PSYKER	This model can attempt to manifest one psychic power in your Psychic phase and attempt to deny one psychic power in your opponent's Psychic phase. It knows *Smite* and one psychic power from the Telethesia discipline (pg 48).

FACTION KEYWORDS	**Imperium, Inquisition, Ordo Malleus**

KEYWORDS	**Character, Infantry, Terminator, Psyker, Agent of the Imperium, Inquisitor**

INQUISITOR

NAME	M	WS	BS	S	T	W	A	Ld	Sv
Inquisitor	6"	3+	3+	3	3	5	4	9	4+

An Inquisitor is a single model equipped with: bolt pistol; chainsword; frag grenades; krak grenades.

WEAPON	RANGE	TYPE	S	AP	D	ABILITIES
Bolt pistol	12"	Pistol 1	4	0	1	-
Chainsword	Melee	Melee	User	0	1	When the bearer fights, it makes 1 additional attack with this weapon.
Frag grenades	6"	Grenade D6	3	0	1	-
Krak grenades	6"	Grenade 1	6	-1	D3	-

WARGEAR OPTIONS
- This model can have the **PSYKER** keyword. If it does, it can be equipped with 1 weapon from the *Force Weapons* list (pg 46) instead of 1 chainsword.
- This model can be equipped with one of the following instead of 1 bolt pistol: 1 weapon from the *Pistol Weapons* list (pg 46), 1 weapon from the *Ranged Weapons* list (pg 46).
- This model can be equipped with 1 weapon from the *Melee Weapons* list (pg 46) instead of 1 chainsword.

ABILITIES

Authority of the Inquisition, Quarry (pg 35)

Refractor Field: This model has a 5+ invulnerable save.

Unquestionable Wisdom: Friendly **IMPERIUM** units can use this model's Leadership characteristic instead of their own whilst they are within 6" of this model.

Iron Will: If this model is not a **PSYKER** and a psychic power manifested by an enemy model targets this model, roll 2D6; if the total is greater than or equal to the Psychic test total, this model is not affected by that power (other models are still affected normally).

PSYKER

If this model is a **PSYKER**, it can attempt to manifest one psychic power in your Psychic phase and attempt to deny one psychic power in your opponent's Psychic phase. It knows *Smite* and one psychic power from the Telethesia discipline (pg 48).

FACTION KEYWORDS IMPERIUM, INQUISITION, <ORDO>

KEYWORDS CHARACTER, INFANTRY, AGENT OF THE IMPERIUM, INQUISITOR

JOKAERO WEAPONSMITH

NAME	M	WS	BS	S	T	W	A	Ld	Sv
Jokaero Weaponsmith	6"	6+	4+	2	3	3	2	7	7+

A Jokaero Weaponsmith is a single model equipped with: Jokaero weapons.

WEAPON	RANGE	TYPE	S	AP	D	ABILITIES
Jokaero weapons	When you choose this weapon to shoot with, select one of the profiles below.					
- Focused strike	24"	Heavy 1	8	-3	3	-
- Scatter shot	12"	Assault 6	4	-1	1	-

ABILITIES

Authority of the Inquisition (pg 35)

Defence Orbs: This model has a 5+ invulnerable save.

Inconceivable Customisation: At the start of your Shooting phase, you can select one friendly <ORDO> unit within 3" of this model and roll one D6; apply the result from the table opposite to the selected unit until the end of the turn.

D6	Result
1-2	**Augmented Targeting:** When resolving an attack made by a model in this unit, you can re-roll the hit roll.
3-4	**Augmented Penetration:** When resolving an attack made by a model in this unit, you can re-roll the wound roll.
5-6	**Total Augmentation:** When resolving an attack made by a model in this unit, you can re-roll the hit roll and you can re-roll the wound roll.

FACTION KEYWORDS IMPERIUM, JOKAERO, INQUISITION, <ORDO>

KEYWORDS CHARACTER, INFANTRY, JOKAERO WEAPONSMITH

ACOLYTES

NAME	M	WS	BS	S	T	W	A	Ld	Sv
Acolyte	6"	4+	4+	3	3	1	2	7	5+

This unit contains 1 Acolyte. It can additionally contain up to 5 additional Acolytes (**Power Rating + 1** per Acolyte). Every model is equipped with: laspistol; chainsword.

WEAPON	RANGE	TYPE	S	AP	D	ABILITIES
Laspistol	12"	Pistol 1	3	0	1	-
Chainsword	Melee	Melee	User	0	1	When the bearer fights, it makes 1 additional attack with this weapon.

WARGEAR OPTIONS	• Any model can be equipped with 1 weapon from the *Pistol Weapons* list (pg 46) instead of 1 laspistol. • Any model can be equipped with 1 weapon from the *Melee Weapons* or *Ranged Weapons* lists (pg 46) instead of 1 chainsword.

ABILITIES	Authority of the Inquisition, Quarry (pg 35) Agent: If this unit contains 1 Acolyte at the start of the battle, it gains the **CHARACTER** keyword.	Loyal Servant: When a friendly <ORDO> INQUISITOR model within 3" of this unit would lose any wounds as a result of an attack made against that model, this unit can attempt to intercept that attack. Roll one D6; on a 2+ that model does not lose those wounds and one model from this unit is destroyed. Only one attempt can be made to intercept each attack.

FACTION KEYWORDS	IMPERIUM, INQUISITION, <ORDO>
KEYWORDS	INFANTRY, ACOLYTES

DAEMONHOST

NAME	M	WS	BS	S	T	W	A	Ld	Sv
Daemonhost	6"	4+	4+	4	4	4	3	7	7+

A Daemonhost is a single model equipped with: unholy gaze; warp grasp.

WEAPON	RANGE	TYPE	S	AP	D	ABILITIES
Unholy gaze	12"	Assault 1	8	-1	1	When resolving an attack made with this weapon, on a wound roll of 6+ this weapon has a Damage characteristic of 3 for that attack.
Warp grasp	Melee	Melee	User	-3	1	-

ABILITIES	**Daemonic Power:** At the start of your Movement phase, roll one D6 for each model with this ability and apply the following result:

D6	Result
1-2	**Daemonic Speed:** Until the start of your next turn, this model has a Move characteristic of 12" and can **FLY**.
3-4	**Re-knit Host Form:** This model regains all its lost wounds.
5-6	**Energy Torrent:** Roll one D6 for each enemy unit within 3" of this model; on a 2+ that enemy unit suffers D3 mortal wounds.

Daemonic: This model has a 5+ invulnerable save.

FACTION KEYWORDS	IMPERIUM, INQUISITION
KEYWORDS	CHARACTER, INFANTRY, DAEMON, DAEMONHOST

ARMOURIES OF THE ORDOS

With near limitless resources, the Inquisition can requisition weaponry from across the Imperium, allowing them to apply the necessary lethality against Humanity's countless foes. From reliable laspistols and chainswords to the arcane and rare inferno pistol and mighty Nemesis Daemon hammer, the wargear of the Inquisition is detailed here.

RANGED WEAPONS

WEAPON	RANGE	TYPE	S	AP	D	ABILITIES
Artificer bolt pistol	12"	Pistol 1	4	-1	2	-
Bolt pistol	12"	Pistol 1	4	0	1	-
Boltgun	24"	Rapid Fire 1	4	0	1	-
Combi-flamer	When you choose this weapon to shoot with, select one or both of the profiles below. If you select both, subtract 1 from hit rolls for attacks made with this weapon.					
- Boltgun	24"	Rapid Fire 1	4	0	1	-
- Flamer	8"	Assault D6	4	0	1	When resolving an attack made with this weapon, do not make a hit roll: it automatically scores a hit.
Combi-melta	When you choose this weapon to shoot with, select one or both of the profiles below. If you select both, subtract 1 from hit rolls for attacks made with this weapon.					
- Boltgun	24"	Rapid Fire 1	4	0	1	-
- Meltagun	12"	Assault 1	8	-4	D6	When resolving an attack made with this weapon against a unit that is within half range, roll two D6 when inflicting damage with it and discard one of the results.
Combi-plasma	When you choose this weapon to shoot with, select one or two of the profiles below. If you select two, subtract 1 from hit rolls for attacks made this weapon. Only one plasma gun profile can be selected.					
- Boltgun	24"	Rapid Fire 1	4	0	1	-
- Plasma gun (standard)	24"	Rapid Fire 1	7	-3	1	-
- Plasma gun (supercharge)	24"	Rapid Fire 1	8	-3	2	If any hit rolls of 1 are made for attacks with this weapon, the bearer is destroyed after shooting with this weapon.
Condemnor boltgun	24"	Rapid Fire 1	4	0	1	When resolving an attack made with this weapon against a **Psyker** unit, this weapon has a Damage characteristic of D3 for that attack.
Dirgesinger	18"	Assault 2	4	0	2	When resolving an attack made with this weapon, on a wound roll of 6+ this weapon has an Armour Penetration characteristic of -3 for that attack.
Electrobane grenades	6"	Grenade 1	4	-1	1	When resolving an attack made with this weapon against a **Vehicle** unit, an unmodified wound roll of 4-5 inflicts 1 mortal wound on the target in addition to any other damage and an unmodified wound roll of 6 inflicts D3 mortal wounds on the target in addition to any other damage.
Jokaero weapons	When you choose this weapon to shoot with, select one of the profiles below.					
- Focused strike	24"	Heavy 1	8	-3	3	-
- Scatter shot	12"	Assault 6	4	-1	1	-
Flamer	8"	Assault D6	4	0	1	When resolving an attack made with this weapon, do not make a hit roll: it automatically scores a hit.
Frag grenades	6"	Grenade D6	3	0	1	-
Hot-shot lasgun	18"	Rapid Fire 1	3	-2	1	-
Incinerator	8"	Assault D6	6	-1	1	When resolving an attack made with this weapon, do not make a hit roll: it automatically scores a hit.
Inferno pistol	6"	Pistol 1	8	-4	D6	When resolving an attack made with this weapon against a unit that is within half range, roll two D6 when inflicting damage with it and discard one of the results.
Laspistol	12"	Pistol 1	3	0	1	-
Krak grenades	6"	Grenade 1	6	-1	D3	-
Master-crafted condemnor boltgun	24"	Rapid Fire 1	4	-1	1	When resolving an attack made with this weapon against a **Psyker** unit, this weapon has a Damage characteristic of 3 for that attack.

RANGED WEAPONS

WEAPON	RANGE	TYPE	S	AP	D	ABILITIES
Master-crafted multi-melta	30"	Assault 1	8	-4	D6	When resolving an attack made with this weapon against a unit that is within half range, roll two D6 when inflicting damage with it and discard one of the results.
Meltagun	12"	Assault 1	8	-4	D6	When resolving an attack made with this weapon against a unit that is within half range, roll two D6 when inflicting damage with it and discard one of the results.
Needle pistol	12"	Pistol 1	1	0	1	When resolving an attack made with this weapon, a wound roll of 6+ is successful if the target is a **Vehicle** unit or **Titanic** unit; otherwise a wound roll of 2+ is successful.
Plasma gun	When you choose this weapon to shoot with, select one of the profiles below.					
- Standard	24"	Rapid Fire 1	7	-3	1	-
- Supercharge	24"	Rapid Fire 1	8	-3	2	If any hit rolls of 1 are made for attacks with this weapon, the bearer is destroyed after shooting with this weapon.
Plasma pistol	When you choose this weapon to shoot with, select one of the profiles below.					
- Standard	12"	Pistol 1	7	-3	1	-
- Supercharge	12"	Pistol 1	8	-3	2	If any hit rolls of 1 are made for attacks with this weapon, the bearer is destroyed after shooting with this weapon.
Psyber-eagle	24"	Assault D6	4	0	1	-
Psycannon	24"	Heavy 4	7	-1	1	-
Psyk-out grenades	6"	Grenade D3	2	0	1	When resolving an attack made with this weapon against a **Psyker** or **Daemon** unit, on a hit roll of 6+ the target suffers 1 mortal wound and the attack sequence ends.
Storm bolter	24"	Rapid Fire 2	4	0	1	-
Unholy gaze	12"	Assault 1	8	-1	1	When resolving an attack made with this weapon, on a wound roll of 6+ this weapon has a Damage characteristic of 3 for that attack.

MELEE WEAPONS

WEAPON	RANGE	TYPE	S	AP	D	ABILITIES
Barbarisater	Melee	Melee	User	-3	D3	When resolving an attack made with this weapon, add 1 to the hit roll.
Chainsword	Melee	Melee	User	0	1	When the bearer fights, it makes 1 additional attack with this weapon.
Force axe	Melee	Melee	+1	-2	D3	-
Force stave	Melee	Melee	+2	-1	D3	-
Force sword	Melee	Melee	User	-3	D3	-
Master-crafted Nemesis Daemon hammer	Melee	Melee	x2	-3	3	-
Master-crafted power sword	Melee	Melee	User	-3	2	-
Nemesis Daemon hammer	Melee	Melee	x2	-3	3	When resolving an attack made with this weapon, subtract 1 from the hit roll.
Power fist	Melee	Melee	x2	-3	D3	When resolving an attack made with this weapon, subtract 1 from the hit roll.
Power maul	Melee	Melee	+2	-1	1	-
Power sword	Melee	Melee	User	-3	1	-
Runestaff	Melee	Melee	+3	-1	D3	-
Throne of Judgement's stomping feet	Melee	Melee	User	-1	2	When the bearer fights, it makes 2D3 additional attacks with this weapon.
Thunder hammer	Melee	Melee	x2	-3	3	When resolving an attack made with this weapon, subtract 1 from the hit roll.
Warp grasp	Melee	Melee	User	-3	1	-

WARGEAR LISTS

MELEE WEAPONS
- Power fist
- Power maul
- Power sword
- Thunder hammer

FORCE WEAPONS
- Force axe
- Force stave
- Force sword
- Nemesis Daemon hammer

PISTOL WEAPONS
- Bolt pistol
- Inferno pistol [1]
- Needle pistol
- Plasma pistol

RANGED WEAPONS
- Boltgun
- Combi-flamer
- Combi-melta
- Combi-plasma

- Condemnor boltgun [1]
- Flamer
- Hot-shot lasgun
- Incinerator [1]
- Meltagun
- Plasma gun
- Storm bolter

[1] **INQUISITOR** only

POINTS VALUES

NAMED CHARACTERS

UNIT	MODELS PER UNIT	POINTS PER MODEL (Including wargear)
Inquisitor Coteaz	1	90
Inquisitor Eisenhorn	1	80
Inquisitor Greyfax	1	85
Inquisitor Karamazov	1	115
Lord Inquisitor Kyria Draxus	1	80

UNITS

UNIT	MODELS PER UNIT	POINTS PER MODEL (Excluding wargear)
Acolytes	1-6	8
Daemonhost	1	25
Inquisitor	1	55
Jokaero Weaponsmith	1	18
Ordo Malleus Inquisitor in Terminator Armour	1	91

RANGED WEAPONS

WEAPON	POINTS PER WEAPON
Bolt pistol	0
Boltgun	0
Combi-flamer	8
Combi-melta	15
Combi-plasma	11
Condemnor boltgun	1
Flamer	6
Frag grenades	0
Hot-shot lasgun	4
Incinerator	20
Inferno pistol	7

RANGED WEAPONS

WEAPON	POINTS PER WEAPON
Jokaero weapons	0
Laspistol	0
Krak grenades	0
Meltagun	14
Needle pistol	2
Plasma gun	11
Plasma pistol	5
Psycannon	7
Psyk-out grenades	0
Storm bolter	2
Unholy gaze	0

MELEE WEAPONS

WEAPON	POINTS PER WEAPON
Chainsword	0
Force axe	10
Force stave	8
Force sword	8
Nemesis Daemon hammer	18
Power fist	9
Power maul	4
Power sword	4
Thunder hammer	16
Warp grasp	0

WARLORD TRAITS

If an **INQUISITION CHARACTER** model is your Warlord, you can use the Inquisition Warlord Traits table to determine what Warlord Trait they have. You can either roll one D3 to randomly generate one, or you can select one. Alternatively, you can select one of the Ordo-specific Warlord Traits below, but only if your Warlord is from the relevant Ordo.

1 RADICAL

They have no qualms about employing tools deemed heretical if it serves Humanity's interests.

Once per battle round, you can re-roll one hit roll, wound roll, damage roll, saving throw, Psychic test or Deny the Witch test made for this Warlord.

2 PURITAN

Their sheer faith in their own righteousness armours them against the horrors of the galaxy.

Improve this Warlord's invulnerable save by 1 (to a maximum of 3+).

3 FORMIDABLE RESOLVE

Their unshakeable will is enough to steel the hearts of Humanity's warriors.

Add 1 to this Warlord's Leadership characteristic and increase the range of this Warlord's Unquestionable Wisdom ability by 6".

ORDO HERETICUS: NO ESCAPE

None can slip their grasp.

This Warlord can perform a Heroic Intervention if there are any enemy units within 6" of them instead of 3", and when doing so can move up to 6" instead of 3". When an enemy unit within 1" of this Warlord is chosen to Fall Back, you can roll one D6; unless any models in that unit have a minimum Move characteristic, on a 4+ that unit cannot Fall Back this turn.

ORDO XENOS: ESOTERIC LORE

Their travels have prepared them for anything.

Whilst this Warlord is on the battlefield, roll one D6 each time your opponent uses a Stratagem; on a 5+ you gain 1 Command Point.

ORDO MALLEUS: PSYCHIC MASTERY

The warp bows to their will.

This Warlord knows one additional psychic power from the Telethesia discipline (pg 48), and can attempt to manifest one additional psychic power in your Psychic phase and attempt to deny one additional psychic power in your opponent's Psychic phase.

NAMED CHARACTERS AND WARLORD TRAITS

If one of the following characters is your Warlord, they must have the associated Warlord Trait shown below:

NAMED CHARACTER	WARLORD TRAIT
Inquisitor Coteaz	Psychic Mastery
Inquisitor Eisenhorn	Radical
Inquisitor Greyfax	No Escape
Inquisitor Karamazov	Formidable Resolve
Lord Inquisitor Kyria Draxus	Radical

TELETHESIA DISCIPLINE

Before the battle, generate the psychic powers for **PSYKER** models that know powers from the Telethesia discipline using the powers presented here. You can either roll one D6 on the table below to generate each power randomly (re-rolling duplicate results), or you can select which powers the psyker knows. If you are selecting powers, you can select from the Ordo-specific powers opposite, but only if the **PSYKER** belongs to that Ordo.

1 TERRIFY

Terrify has a warp charge value of 6. If manifested, select one enemy unit within 18" of, and visible to, this psyker. Until the start of your next Psychic phase, subtract 1 from the Leadership characteristic of models in that unit and that unit cannot fire Overwatch.

2 PSYCHIC FORTITUDE

Psychic Fortitude has a warp charge value of 4. If manifested, select one friendly **IMPERIUM** unit within 12" of this psyker. Until the start of your next Psychic phase, when a Morale test is taken for that unit, do not roll the dice; it is automatically passed.

3 DOMINATE

Dominate has a warp charge value of 6. If manifested, select one enemy model within 12" of this psyker that is not a **VEHICLE** and roll 3D6. If the total is equal to or greater than that enemy model's Leadership characteristic, that enemy model can immediately shoot with one weapon as if it were your Shooting phase, or make one attack as if it were the Fight phase. In either case, treat that enemy model as if it is a separate unit that is part of your army whilst shooting or making that close combat attack.

4 MENTAL INTERROGATION

Mental Interrogation has a warp charge value of 6. If manifested, select one enemy **CHARACTER** model within 12" of, and visible to, this psyker. Until the start of your next Psychic phase, when resolving an attack made by that enemy model, subtract 1 from the hit roll. If your army is Battle-forged roll 3D6; if the result is equal to or greater than that enemy model's Leadership characteristic, you gain 1 Command Point.

5 PSYCHIC PURSUIT

Psychic Pursuit has a warp charge value of 7. If manifested, select one enemy **CHARACTER** unit that only contains models with a Wounds characteristic of less than 10 and is within 18" of, and visible to, this psyker. Then, select one friendly <**ORDO**> Infantry unit within 6" of this psyker. Until the end of your next Shooting phase, that <**ORDO**> Infantry unit can target that **CHARACTER** unit, even if it is not the closest enemy unit.

6 CASTIGATION

Castigation has a warp charge value of 6. If manifested, select one enemy unit within 18" of, and visible to, this psyker and roll 3D6; if the total exceeds the lowest Leadership characteristic in that enemy unit, that enemy unit suffers D3 mortal wounds.

ORDO HERETICUS: SCOURGING

The psyker fashions a lash from their foe's own guilt and uses it to flay their writhing minds.

Scourging has a warp charge value of 6. If manifested, select one enemy unit within 12" of this psyker. Until the start of your next Psychic phase, subtract 1 from the Attacks characteristic of models in that enemy unit (to a minimum of 1). Roll 2D6; if the total is equal to or greater than the highest Leadership characteristic in that enemy unit, then until the start of your next Psychic phase, when resolving an attack made by a model in that enemy unit, subtract 1 from the hit roll.

ORDO XENOS: PSYCHIC VEIL

The psyker conjures a glamour to shield their allies.

Psychic Veil has a warp charge value of 5. If manifested, until the start of your next Psychic phase, friendly **ORDO XENOS** units within 6" of this psyker can only be selected as the target of attacks if they are the closest visible enemy unit, and can only be selected as the target of charges if they are within 6" of the charging unit.

ORDO MALLEUS: WARDING INCANTATION

The psyker chants a protective invocation, raising a wall of adjuratory empyric wards around their allies.

Warding Incantation has a warp charge value of 6. If manifested, select one friendly **IMPERIUM INFANTRY** or **IMPERIUM BIKER** unit within 12" of this psyker. Until the start of your next Psychic phase, models in that unit have a 5+ invulnerable save.

RELICS OF THE INQUISITION

Many and rare are the treasures, the antiquities and the proscribed artefacts that fill the armouries of the Inquisition. Some shine with a blessed radiance, while others stem from darker provenance.

If your army is led by an **INQUISITION** Warlord, you can give one of the following Relics of the Inquisition to an **INQUISITION CHARACTER** model from your army. Named characters and **VEHICLE** models cannot be given any of the following Relics.

Note that some Relics are weapons that replace one of the model's existing weapons. Where this is the case, you must, if you are using points values, still pay the cost of the weapon that is being replaced. Write down any Relics of the Inquisition your models have on your army roster.

BLADE OF THE ORDO

Many Inquisitors have commissioned or acquired masterwork power blades. No two such weapons are ever exactly alike, but all are potent martial tools.

INQUISITOR model equipped with power sword only. This Relic replaces a power sword and has the following profile:

WEAPON	RANGE	TYPE	S	AP	D
Blade of the Ordo	Melee	Melee	+1	-3	D3

Abilities: When resolving an attack made with this weapon against a unit that is specified by the bearer's Quarry ability (pg 35), this weapon has a Damage characteristic of 3 for that attack.

DIGITAL WEAPONS

These potent, short-ranged energy weapons are concealed in precious items of jewellery, the better to lethally surprise the foe.

INQUISITOR model only. When a model with this Relic fights, it can make 1 additional attack using the close combat weapon profile (see the *Warhammer 40,000* rulebook). When resolving that attack, if a hit is scored the target suffers 1 mortal wound and the attack sequence ends.

BLACKSHROUD

First recorded in the possession of the enigmatic Inquisitor Thastrobel, this whisp-like shroud renders its wearer as insubstantial as a warp-wraith.

INQUISITOR model only. When resolving an attack made against a model with this Relic, subtract 1 from the wound roll.

IGNIS JUDICIUM

The flames of this ancient inferno pistol burn hottest when engulfing the heretic and the witch. Theirs is a conflagration only absolution can extinguish.

ORDO HERETICUS INQUISITOR model equipped with inferno pistol only. This Relic replaces an inferno pistol and has the following profile:

WEAPON	RANGE	TYPE	S	AP	D
Ignis Judicium	12"	Pistol 1	8	-4	D6

Abilities: When resolving an attack made with this weapon against a unit that is within half range or that has the **CHAOS** or **PSYKER** keyword, roll two D6 when inflicting damage with it and discard one of the results.

UNIVERSAL ANATHEMA

A fragment of STC technology, this device tastes the bio-spoor of its owner's foes, then fashions tailored toxins not even the most resilient victim can long endure.

ORDO XENOS INQUISITOR model only. When resolving an attack made with a melee weapon by a model with this Relic against a unit that is not a **VEHICLE** or **TITANIC**, a wound roll of 2+ is always successful.

TAINTED BLADE

Only the most radical Inquisitor would bear such an accursed weapon, risking the wilful malevolence of the entity trapped within so as to unleash its bound might against the Emperor's enemies.

ORDO MALLEUS INQUISITOR model equipped with power sword only. This Relic replaces a power sword and has the following profile:

WEAPON	RANGE	TYPE	S	AP	D
Tainted Blade	Melee	Melee	+3	-3	1

Abilities: In the Fight phase, when the bearer is chosen to fight with for the first time that phase, roll one D6; on a 1 the bearer suffers 1 mortal wound and this weapon cannot be used that phase. When resolving an attack made with this weapon, if the saving throw is failed you can make one additional attack against the same unit using this weapon. This additional attack cannot generate another attack.

STRATAGEMS

If your army is Battle-forged and includes any Inquisitor units, you have access to the Stratagems shown here and can spend Command Points to activate them. These reflect the unique strategies used by the Inquisition. If a Stratagem is used before the battle to upgrade a unit (e.g. Arbiter of the Emperor's Will) and you have an army roster, you must note on it which Stratagems are used to upgrade which units.

EXECUTION BOMBARDMENT
4CP
Inquisition Stratagem

Once an Inquisitor has passed judgement upon their quarry, there is no limit to the magnitude of weaponry they can bring to bear against them.

Use this Stratagem in your Shooting phase, if an **Inquisitor** model from your army is on the battlefield. Select one point on the battlefield and roll one D6 for each unit within 2D6" of that point, subtracting 1 from the result if the unit being rolled for is a **Character**. On a 4+ the unit being rolled for suffers D3 mortal wounds. You can only use this Stratagem once per battle.

ARBITER OF THE EMPEROR'S WILL
1CP
Inquisition Stratagem

Such is the power conveyed by the Inquisitorial mandate that every agent of the Ordos acts with the implicit authority of the Emperor himself.

Use this Stratagem before the battle. Select one **Inquisitor** model from your army that is not your Warlord and determine one Warlord Trait for it; it is regarded as your Warlord for the purposes of that Warlord Trait. If that model is not a named character or **Vehicle**, you can then give one Relic of the Inquisition to that model. All of the Relics your army includes must be different and be given to different models. You can only use this Stratagem once per battle.

STRATEGIC EXCRUCIATION
1CP
Inquisition Stratagem

There is a horrible art to the battlefield interrogation of captured foes. It must be done swiftly and with the greatest efficacy, for prying loose the enemy's secrets by any means is often the key to victory.

Use this Stratagem in any phase, after an enemy **Character** unit is destroyed within 3" of any **Inquisition** units from your army. Gain D3 Command Points and subtract 1 from the Leadership characteristic of enemy units until the end of the battle. You can only use this Stratagem once per battle.

ALPHA-CLASS PSYKER
1CP
Inquisition Stratagem

While many Inquisitors possess psychic abilities, some are so ferociously powerful that they are considered abominations by their more puritan peers.

Use this Stratagem before the battle. Select one **Psyker Inquisitor** model from your army that is not a named character. This model knows one additional psychic power from the Telethesia discipline, and can attempt to deny one additional psychic power in your opponent's Psychic phase. You can only use this Stratagem once per battle.

TO THE EXCLUSION OF ALL ELSE...
1CP
Inquisition Stratagem

When an Inquisitor sights their quarry, they command all nearby allies to concentrate upon them.

Use this Stratagem in your Shooting phase, the Fight phase or your opponent's Charge phase, when an **Imperium Infantry** or **Imperium Biker** unit from your army that is within 6" of a friendly **Inquisitor** unit fires Overwatch or is chosen to shoot or fight with. Until the end of that phase, when resolving an attack made by a model in that unit against an enemy unit specified in that **Inquisitor** unit's Quarry ability (pg 35), re-roll a hit roll of 1.

CLANDESTINE OPERATION
1CP
Inquisition Stratagem

Often an Inquisitor will work undercover, only revealing themselves when the moment is right.

Use this Stratagem during deployment. Select one **Infantry Inquisitor** unit and up to one **Acolyte**, up to one **Daemonhost** and up to one **Jokaero** units. These units can be set up anywhere on the battlefield that is more than 9" away from any enemy deployment zones, but all models set up in this way must be set up within 6" of the selected **Inquisitor** unit. You can only use this Stratagem once per battle.

INQUISITION NAME GENERATOR

Inquisitors and their henchmen are drawn from all across the incalculably vast span of the Imperium, and even beyond. Their names are as varied and strange as the cultures they hail from. The table below provides examples and inspiration with which to name your own Inquisition models. If you wish to randomly generate a name, you can roll a D66 and consult the table below. To roll a D66, simply roll two D6, one after the other – the first represents tens, and the second represents digits, giving you a result between 11 and 66.

D66	FIRST NAME		D66	LAST NAME
11	Arcturus		11	O'fane
12	Callenia		12	Incendario
13	Th'emach		13	Vance
14	Othia		14	Theng
15	Zann		15	Jachus
16	Kyphus		16	Caldori
21	Bastovalius		21	Yarvwe
22	Che		22	Tassus
23	Guideon		23	Pho
24	Persephona		24	Heng
25	Chunhue		25	VanKallus
26	Alexia		26	Mardane
31	Thuomas		31	Klenger
32	Lorne		32	Nassemio
33	Drast		33	Thale
34	Dellovorn		34	Achitor
35	Hotakun		35	III
36	Aspoverimus		36	Weisser
41	Launcel		41	Hasetandrus
42	Kericha		42	Abastus-Hesp
43	Masegou		43	Kallovich
44	T'sung		44	Achebae
45	Borian		45	Watanake
46	Taph		46	Sollus
51	Zandrigal		51	Kaur
52	Unguos		52	Gethsemanus
53	Korsipher		53	Tyroh
54	Mattus		54	Skrave'Ghanash
55	Phe'vol		55	Pahllas
56	Saskiah		56	Decimus
61	Ignatius		61	Kleng
62	Mordreth		62	Dox
63	Olufemhi		63	the Faceless
64	Kassandra		64	Shen'bau
65	Lorgh		65	Iso
66	Massimeo		66	Vierbech

HEROES & VILLAINS

'The galaxy teems with
quarrelsome insects, possessed
of rudimentary sentience yet
believing themselves great,
laughably ill-equipped for the
godhead to which they presume.
They have had their day. Now, as
once before, it is our time...'

- Illuminor Szeras

EPHRAEL STERN AND KYGANIL OF THE BLOODY TEARS

Amongst all the countless warriors of the Adepta Sororitas, Ephrael Stern is unique. Driven by a strange destiny and possessed of formidable powers that many call heretical, she and her Aeldari comrade Kyganil have cut a swathe through some of the great and terrible events of this dark millennium.

Ephrael Stern has been known by many terms during her long years in service to the God-Emperor – Thrice-born, Daemonifuge, sainted saviour, heretical witch.

Once, she had been a respected and accomplished Seraphim within the Order of Our Martyred Lady, but fate had greater things in store for Ephrael Stern. It was on Parnis, during an expedition to discover the fate of the lost Order Pronatus, that Stern was slain in battle against the minions of a Slaaneshi Greater Daemon. This same Daemon had taken the seven hundred sisters of the Order Pronatus and forged them into a single, eternally suffering flesh-prison it called the Screaming Cage. Yet while its punishment magnified the pain of those damned sisters, it also fused their mental might and faith.

Seizing their chance, the entities of the Screaming Cage poured all of their powers into Stern's fallen form and propelled her back to life, as a tremendously powerful and gifted champion against the servants of Chaos.

Since that day, Ephrael Stern has had to battle not only the worshippers of the Dark Gods, but also those of her own Imperium who believe her to be irrevocably tainted. Though they might find their fuel in faith, Stern's powers manifest themselves in a supernatural fashion that many have mistaken for – or chosen to perceive and condemn as – witchery. She is stronger and faster than any of her sisters, can unleash searing bolts of holy judgement upon her foes and, when death has claimed her, she has returned to life once again. In this era of proliferating psychic mutation and untrammelled heresy, such supernatural occurrences are more than enough to render Stern a target for more than one firebrand zealot.

Nor is she helped by the company she keeps. Bound together by the strands of fate, she travels with an Aeldari known as Kyganil, or simply the Pariah. Once, this fey warrior was a Harlequin of the Laughing God; now he is a wanderer, an outcast from his own people who has found his place at Stern's side. Kyganil has brought her by dark paths to the repository of forbidden lore known as the Black Library, and it is through him that Stern has made contact with the Ynnari – though none but she yet know her true purpose in this.

EPHRAEL STERN AND KYGANIL OF THE BLOODY TEARS

NAME	M	WS	BS	S	T	W	A	Ld	Sv
Ephrael Stern	7"	2+	3+	4	4	6	4	9	3+
Kyganil	8"	2+	3+	3	3	5	4	9	6+

This unit contains 1 Ephrael Stern and 1 Kyganil. Ephrael Stern is equipped with: bolt pistol; Sanctity; frag grenades; krak grenades. Kyganil is equipped with: Harlequin's kiss; The Outcast's Blades; plasma grenades. You can only include one of this unit in your army.

WEAPON	RANGE	TYPE	S	AP	D	ABILITIES
Bolt pistol	12"	Pistol 1	4	0	1	-
Harlequin's kiss	Melee	Melee	+1	-1	D3	-
The Outcast's Blades	Melee	Melee	User	-1	1	Make 2 hit rolls for each attack made with this weapon instead of 1.
Sanctity	Melee	Melee	+1	-3	2	-
Frag grenades	6"	Grenade D6	3	0	1	-
Krak grenades	6"	Grenade 1	6	-1	D3	-
Plasma grenades	6"	Grenade D6	4	-1	1	-

ABILITIES	
	Cast Together by Fate: During deployment, both models in this unit must be set up at the same time, though they do not need to be set up in unit coherency. From that point onwards, each model is treated as a separate unit.
	Unexpected Allies: This unit can be included in any IMPERIUM Detachment without taking up a slot, as long as every unit in your army (with the exception of those that are UNALIGNED) has the IMPERIUM keyword (and does not have the FALLEN keyword). This unit does not prevent other units from your army from benefiting from Detachment abilities (e.g. Chapter Tactics, Canticles of the Omnissiah), and does not prevent units from gaining abilities that require every model in your army to have that ability (e.g. Combat Doctrines). In a matched play game, these models are ignored for the purposes of the Battle Brothers rule (although all units from your army must still have the IMPERIUM Faction keyword).
	Wanderers: Neither Ephrael Stern nor Kyganil can be your Warlord. In addition, during deployment, you can set up these models in the webway instead of setting them up on the battlefield. If you do, at the end of one of your Movement phases you can set up these models anywhere on the battlefield within 3" of each other and more than 9" away from any enemy models.
ABILITIES (EPHRAEL STERN)	**Daemonifuge:** At the start of your Shooting phase, roll 2D6, adding 2 to the result if there are any CHAOS units within 18" of Ephrael Stern. On a 5+, the nearest enemy unit that is within 18" of and visible to Ephrael Stern suffers D3 mortal wounds (if the result is 9 or more, that unit instead suffers D6 mortal wounds).
	Divine Protection: This model has a 4+ invulnerable save. In addition, when resolving an attack against this model, subtract 1 from the hit roll.
ABILITIES (KYGANIL)	**Knight of Shadows:** This model has a 4+ invulnerable save. In addition, this model can fight first in the Fight phase, even if it did not make a charge move that turn. If your opponent has units that did make a charge move that turn, or that have a similar ability, then alternate choosing units to fight with, starting with the player whose turn is taking place.
	Mysterious Saviour: Whilst this model is within 3" of a friendly EPHRAEL STERN model, roll one D6 each time that model would lose a wound; on a 5+ that wound is not lost.
FACTION KEYWORDS	**IMPERIUM**
KEYWORDS (EPHRAEL STERN)	**ADEPTA SORORITAS, CHARACTER, INFANTRY, EPHRAEL STERN**
KEYWORDS (KYGANIL)	**AELDARI, CHARACTER, INFANTRY, KYGANIL**

POINTS VALUES

UNIT	MODELS PER UNIT	POINTS PER UNIT (Including wargear)
Ephrael Stern and Kyganil	2	115

ILLUMINOR SZERAS

Illuminor Szeras is a merciless monster, a bioarchitect and hypertechnological vivisector who seeks to unpick the secrets of life itself. He puts his anatomical knowledge to use both on and off the battlefield, preying upon living specimens to better refine and enhance the Necron form.

The C'tan might have provided the knowledge for biotransference, but it was Szeras who made it a reality. Even then, he saw it as the first of several steps on the path to ultimate evolution – a journey that would end with a creature not of flesh or metal, but with a god of pure energy. Until that day, Szeras is driven to take full advantage of his android form, and labour constantly to improve upon its functionality. After all, no longer must he sleep nor deal with the thousand frailties and distractions of the flesh.

Szeras labours to unravel the mysteries of life, for he fears that he would be a poor god without such secrets at his fingertips. Szeras has been on the brink of understanding for many centuries, yet somehow final comprehension always escapes him. Perhaps there are some concepts in the universe that do not reveal themselves before logic, be those matters of the soul or of the ineffable power of faith. Whatever the reason, such secrets will almost certainly lie forever beyond Szeras' comprehension.

This is a truth he will never accept, however. It is a fact that has, of late, provided the shadowy Silent King with the leverage required to secure Szeras' allegiance. After all, if the Illuminor wrought biotransference to begin with then surely he could reverse the process' effects and perhaps, in doing so, garner the final revelations that he has sought for so long?

Whoever's interests he serves, Szeras often haunts the battlefields of the 41st Millennium like a ghoul. He requires a constant flow of living subjects, and the most efficient way for him to acquire such creatures is to trade his expertise in exchange for captives. Though Szeras is obsessed with the secrets of life, his aptitude for augmenting Necron weaponry, and even mechanical bodies, is peerless. Szeras' delving into the form and function of so many disparate living creatures has taught him how to improve almost every facet of Necron machinery – a trait that is seen as distasteful by many of his peers. The dissection of Vuzsalen Arachtoid compound eyes unlocked an improved array for targeting optics, and the molecular disassembling of chitinous Ambull hide led the way to more efficient armour configurations, to name but two of many thousands of such advances.

It is a matter of some speculation how much involvement Szeras had in the design and implementation of the Pariah Nexus, but none can question that he is taking full advantage of the effects. Hundreds of thousands of stilled beings have already vanished into the Illuminor's horrific laboratories, and his harvest continues apace.

ILLUMINOR SZERAS

NAME	M	WS	BS	S	T	W	A	Ld	Sv
Illuminor Szeras	8"	3+	3+	6	6	7	4	10	3+

Illuminor Szeras is a single model equipped with: eldritch lance; impaling legs. You can only include one **ILLUMINOR SZERAS** model in your army.

WEAPON	RANGE	TYPE	S	AP	D	ABILITIES
Eldritch lance (Shooting)	18"	Assault D3	8	-4	D6	-
Eldritch lance (Melee)	Melee	Melee	+1	-3	2	-
Impaling legs	Melee	Melee	User	-2	1	When the bearer fights, it makes 2 additional attacks with this weapon.

ABILITIES

Living Metal: At the start of each of your turns, this model regains 1 lost wound.

Master Technomancer: Add 1 to rolls made for the Reanimation Protocols ability of friendly **NECRONS** units within 3" of this model. A unit cannot benefit from both the Master Technomancer and Technomancer abilities in the same turn.

Atomic Energy Manipulator: If this model destroys one or more enemy units in the Fight phase, then at the end of that phase it can use its Mechanical Augmentation ability as if it were the end of your Movement phase.

Empyric Overcharger: When a Psychic test is taken for an enemy **PSYKER** within 9" of this model, that enemy **PSYKER** suffers Perils of the Warp on any dice roll that includes a double, instead of only a double 1 or double 6.

Mechanical Augmentation: At the end of your Movement phase, you can select one **NECRON WARRIORS** or **IMMORTALS** unit from your army that is within 6" of this model and has not already been affected by this ability this battle. If you do so, roll one D3 and consult the table below:

D3	AUGMENTATION
1	Add 1 to the Strength characteristic of models in that unit until the end of the battle.
2	Add 1 to the Toughness characteristic of models in that unit until the end of the battle.
3	Improve the Ballistic Skill characteristic of models in that unit by 1 until the end of the battle (e.g. Ballistic Skill 3+ becomes 2+).

FACTION KEYWORDS	**NECRONS**

KEYWORDS	**CHARACTER, INFANTRY, CRYPTEK, ILLUMINOR SZERAS**

POINTS VALUES

UNIT	MODELS PER UNIT	POINTS PER MODEL (Including wargear)
Illuminor Szeras	1	130

THEATRES OF WAR

'We inhabit a galaxy of infinite wonders, or so they say. In my experience this translates to planet upon planet of inventively horrible environments, each more inhospitable and bizarre to fight across than the last. It is hardly something to celebrate…'

- *Rogue Trader Eli Deplatus*

THEATRE OF WAR
THE WEBWAY

Using these rules you can transform your battlefield into a warp-ravaged spar of the webway, as depicted in *Psychic Awakening: Phoenix Rising*.

When fighting a battle in the webway, the following rules apply:

EPHEMERAL INTERFERENCE

Strange energies and ghostly winds buffet those fighting here, stealing away the furious energies of their weapons.

When resolving an attack made with a ranged weapon against a target not within 12", reduce the Armour Penetration characteristic of that weapon by 1, to a minimum of 0, for that attack (e.g. AP -1 becomes AP 0).

GHOSTBLADES

Whether by accident or design, the unpredictable energies of the webway bind themselves to the blades of those fighting here. Coiling mists stream behind weapons until blades, fists and axes flicker as insubstantially as the vapours around them. They prove solid enough with each blow they land, however…

When resolving an attack made with a melee weapon, an unmodified hit roll of 6 automatically scores a hit and successfully wounds the target (do not make a wound roll).

BATTLEFIELD TWISTS

Before the battle, one player rolls one D3 and consults the battlefield twists table below, or both players can agree on the most suitable option. The result is an additional rule for the battle. This roll cannot be re-rolled.

D3	BATTLEFIELD TWIST
1	**The Labyrinth Dimension:** *Becoming lost amidst the twists and turns of the webway is all too likely. Its passages and portals intertwine through one another to form an organic, fractal maze with a will of its own.* In the first and second battle rounds, units that are set up on the battlefield as reinforcements are not set up as normal. Instead, you must roll one D6 for each unit before setting it up on the battlefield. On a 4+, set that unit up as normal; otherwise, that unit is not set up that battle round.
2	**Shattered Spar:** *This portion of the webway is sorely damaged, reality flickering within its bounds and the anarchy of the empyrean spilling through.* Players cannot gain, or be refunded, Command Points.
3	**Zephyrstride Matrix:** *Eldritch technologies hasten the footfalls of those who battle here, speeding them into combat.* When an Advance or charge roll is made for a unit, add 1 to the result.

MYSTERIOUS OBJECTIVE MARKERS

If you are using any objective markers, before determining deployment zones, one player should roll one D3 and consult the mysterious objective markers table below, or both players can agree on the most suitable option. The result is an additional rule applied to all objective markers for the battle. This roll cannot be re-rolled.

D3	MYSTERIOUS OBJECTIVE MARKER
1	**Runic Seal:** *Such Aeldari runes hold back the surging energies of the warp, warding the area around them.* Models have a 5+ invulnerable save whilst within 3" of an objective marker.
2	**Psionic Nodal Conduit:** *Acting in a similar fashion to the infinity circuits of the Craftworlds, micro-crystalline relays allow psychic energies to pass from one node to the next.* When resolving a Psychic power manifested by a model from your army within 6" of any objective markers, you can select one objective marker on the battlefield. If you do so, when determining visibility and measuring distances for that psychic power, determine both from the selected objective marker rather than from the model.
3	**Empyric Syphon:** *Though not intended for such use, this crystalline structure can be used to channel warp energies.* In the Psychic phase, **PSYKER** models can attempt to manifest one additional psychic power whilst within 6" of any objective markers.

TERRAIN TRAITS

Before the battle, one player should roll one D3 and consult the terrain traits table below, or both players can agree on the most suitable option. The result is an additional rule applied to the specified terrain features for the battle, other than **BUILDING** units. This roll cannot be re-rolled.

D3	TERRAIN TRAIT
1	**Ethereal Constructs:** *Illusory and spectral, the ghosts of realspace battlefields shimmer in and out of view in this region, conjured by a weakening in the weave of the webway itself.* At the start of the battle round, each player nominates three different terrain features on the battlefield. Roll one D6 to randomly select one of those terrain features. Until the end of that battle round, models cannot gain the benefit of cover from the selected terrain feature.
2	**Psycho-crystalline Transduction Circuit:** *Here, otherworldly structures meld with the walls of the webway, glimmering with psionic amplification circuitry.* When a Psychic test is taken for a model within 6" of a Ruins terrain feature, add 1 to the total.
3	**Maze of Future Lamentations:** *Weird, shrine-like structures wrought in crystal and living bone flicker here, the mists that wind about them depicting warnings of tragic events still to come in the lives of those who witness them.* Units entirely within a Ruins terrain feature at the start of the Fight phase can fight first in that phase, even if they did not make a charge move that turn. If both players have units that have a similar ability or made a charge move that turn, then alternate choosing units to fight with, starting with the player whose turn is taking place.

STRATAGEMS

If your army is Battle-forged, you have access to the Stratagems shown below whilst using this Theatre of War.

2CP — INHERITORS OF THE WEBWAY
Webway Stratagem
The Aeldari are at home amidst these ethereal confines.

Use this Stratagem at the start of the first battle round. Select up to three **AELDARI** units from your army. Those units can make a move as if it were your Movement phase, but cannot Advance and must end that move more than 9" away from any enemy models. You can only use this Stratagem once per battle.

2CP — ARTERIAL LINKWAY
Webway Stratagem
By braving the webway's maze-like passages it is possible to outmanoeuvre your foes in impossible ways.

Use this Stratagem at the start of your Movement phase. Select one unit from your army wholly within 6" of any battlefield edge. Remove that unit from the battlefield. At the end of your next Movement phase, set that unit up anywhere on the battlefield wholly within 6" of any battlefield edge and more than 6" away from any enemy models.

Many of the worlds around Talledus – the setting for *Psychic Awakening: Faith and Fury* – boasted fortified cathedrum complexes that saw fierce and destructive fighting. Using these rules you can transform your tabletop battlefield into a uniquely Imperial blend of Ecclesiarchal Ruins and sanctified Fortifications.

Designer's Note: *If playing using this Theatre of War, we recommend that the battlefield features plenty of Wall of Martyrs defence lines, emplacements and bunkers as terrain features, as well as Ruins to represent shattered shrines. These should be set up so that both players have an equal chance to capture and use them, rather than them being set up as part of a player's army.*

When fighting a battle upon a war-torn shrine world, the following rules apply:

CONSTANT BOMBARDMENT

Forming the focal point for furious urban warfare, the blasted ruins of this once-proud shrine complex are pummelled by endless waves of falling munitions.

At the start of each player's Shooting phase, that player can select up to three enemy units (**CHARACTERS** cannot be selected unless they are a **VEHICLE** or **MONSTER**) and roll one D6 for each unit. On a 1-4, nothing happens. On a 5, that unit suffers 1 mortal wound. On a 6, that unit suffers D3 mortal wounds.

BATTLEFIELD TWISTS

Before the battle, one player rolls one D6 and consults the battlefield twists table below, or both players can agree on the most suitable option. The result is an additional rule for the battle. This roll cannot be re-rolled.

D6	BATTLEFIELD TWIST
1	**Prepared Positions:** *The faithful prepared their defences well here, but some have since been seized by their foes. Now both sides benefit from protective measures that serve to drag the conflict on into a grinding stalemate.* Units wholly within the controlling player's deployment zone (other than **TITANIC** or **AIRCRAFT** units) receive the benefit of cover, even while they are not entirely on or within a terrain feature. A unit loses this benefit the first time it makes a move of any kind (e.g. normal move, charge move, pile in etc.).
2	**Auto-martyrdom:** *This entire region has been seeded with mines by zealous troopers who believe that the Emperor guides the footfalls of the faithful, claiming only those whose time he deems to have come.* Roll one D6 each time a unit Advances or makes a charge move; on a 1, that unit suffers 1 mortal wound.
3	**Fortified Catacombs:** *The halls of the sainted dead proliferate beneath the battlefield, and can be accessed through tunnels and blasted stairways. Troops can slink through these sepulchres to ambush the foe.* During deployment, each player can select one **INFANTRY** or **SWARM** unit from their army. They can set up this unit in a forgotten tunnel instead of setting it up on the battlefield. If they do, at the end of one of that player's Movement phases, they can set up the selected unit anywhere on the battlefield that is more than 9" away from any enemy models.
4	**Darkened Skies:** *The fires of countless pyres and perpetual war have ensured that this world's skies are filled with smoke, vast clouds of which drift across the battlefield, periodically obscuring combatants from view.* At the start of the battle round, the player going first rolls one D6; on a 5+, until the end of the battle, you cannot select an **INFANTRY** or **SWARM** unit as the target of a ranged attack unless it is within 18" of the firing unit.
5	**Aura of the Humble Saints:** *Psychic mutation runs rampant through this region, likely the cause of the bloody conflict now tearing it apart. For all the damage it has provoked, the swelling tide of background psychic energy enhances the abilities of psykers across the battlefield.* When a Psychic test is taken for a **PSYKER** that is within 3" of an objective marker, add 1 to the total.
6	**The Emperor Protects with Ferrocrete and Iron:** *Despite its derelict appearance, this area is filled with sturdy ruins that provide excellent protection.* When resolving an attack with a ranged weapon against a unit that is receiving the benefit of cover to their saving throw from Ruins, if the weapon being used for that attack has an Armour Penetration characteristic of -1, treat this as 0 instead.

MYSTERIOUS OBJECTIVE MARKERS

The first time each objective marker is controlled by any player at the end of a battle round, that player rolls one D6; on a 6, that objective marker is a mysterious objective. That player then rolls a D3 and consults the mysterious objective markers table below to discover what ability that objective has. The result is an additional rule applied to that objective marker for the battle. These rolls cannot be re-rolled.

D3	MYSTERIOUS OBJECTIVE MARKER
1	**Altar of War:** *Whether defending its sanctity or despoiling it, warriors fight all the more viciously around this blessed location.* If your army controls this objective marker at the start of your Shooting phase, you can select one unit from your army that is within 3" of this objective marker. Add 1 to wound rolls for attacks made with Heavy weapons by models in that unit if the firing model Remained Stationary in your preceding Movement phase.
2	**Defensible Locale:** *Be it choral data-shrines or artfully laid out sight-line blocking cloisters, Imperial cathedrums are often more defensible than they first appear.* If you control this objective marker at the start of your Shooting phase, you can select one unit from your army that is within 3" of it. Re-roll hit rolls of 1 for attacks made with ranged weapons by models in that unit until the end of that phase.
3	**Holy Relic:** *An aura of divinity radiates from this ancient relic, driving those nearby into ecstasies of fervour or hatred.* At the start of the Morale phase, the player whose army controls this objective marker can select one unit from their army that is within 3" of this objective marker. Add 2 to the Leadership characteristic of models in that unit until the end of that phase.

STRATAGEMS

If your army is Battle-forged, you have access to the Stratagems shown below whilst using this Theatre of War.

1CP

SUPERIOR CONSTRUCTION
War-torn Shrine World Stratagem

As one would expect of a mighty Ecclesiarchal cathedrum – even a ruined one – the fortifications found amidst this structure are built to the highest quality.

Use this Stratagem when you set up a **Building** model on the battlefield. Add 4 to that model's Wounds characteristic.

2CP

MALFUNCTIONING AUTO-DEFENSORS
War-torn Shrine World Stratagem

Some areas of the cathedrum still contain damaged weapon servitors or defensive auto-turrets, originally installed to corral pilgrims or guard relics. These sporadically wake before powering down again.

Use this Stratagem at the start of any battle round. Select one terrain feature on the battlefield. Until the end of that battle round, at the end of the Movement phase, roll one D6 for each unit that is within 3" of that terrain feature. On a 6, that unit suffers D3 mortal wounds.

DEVOURED WORLD

When the Gracinth Pontus System was declared lost to Hive Fleet Leviathan, several last ditch efforts were made to retrieve vital relics, intelligence and personnel from under the nose of the Tyranid invaders. The rules found here allow you to fight battles amongst these deadly environs, and can easily be used to represent fighting upon a world in the last stages of Tyranid ingestion, as shown in *Psychic Awakening: Blood of Baal.*

When fighting a battle on a devoured world, the following rules apply:

PSYCHIC BLACKOUT

The concentrated effect of the Shadow in the Warp smothers and chokes off the abilities of even the most potent battle-psykers. It is all they can do not to lose their minds.

When making a Psychic test, roll one additional D6 and discard the highest roll. If both dice results are the same, select one of them to discard. **TYRANID** models are not affected by this ability.

DIGESTIVE SPORES

The air is rendered thick and soupy by clouds of deadly spores that settle in the slightest nick or cut and rapidly begin breaking down the living matter of their victim for ingestion.

At the end of the battle round, roll one D6 for each model from your army that is on the battlefield and has any lost wounds. On a 1 or 2, that model suffers 1 mortal wound.

STRATAGEMS

If your army is Battle-forged, you have access to the Stratagems shown below whilst using this Theatre of War.

2CP — SYNAPSE NODES
Devoured World Stratagem

Seeded across the planet, these unassuming pods provide an anchor for the synaptic control of lesser tyranid bioforms.

Use this Stratagem at the start of the first battle round. Until the end of the battle, **TYRANID** units that are within 3" of any objective markers are treated as being within 24" of a **<HIVE FLEET> SYNAPSE** unit for the purposes of the Instinctive Behaviour ability.

1CP — FRACTURED ENVIRONMENT
Devoured World Stratagem

The introduction of Tyranid spores and toxins produces varying effects depending on local atmospheric elements.

If you are using Battlefield Twists for this battle, you can use this Stratagem after deployment, but before the first battle round. You can either replace the current Battlefield Twist with one of your choice, or randomly generate one additional Battlefield Twist to be in effect this battle. This Stratagem can only be used once per battle by each player.

BATTLEFIELD TWISTS

Before the battle, one player rolls one D6 and consults the battlefield twists table below, or both players can agree on the most suitable option. The result is an additional rule for the battle. This roll cannot be re-rolled.

D6	BATTLEFIELD TWIST
1	**Drifting Spore Mines:** *As the planet's atmosphere is slowly consumed, errant spore mines drift on dying winds across the battlefield.* At the end of the battle round, after rolling for the Digestive Spores rule, randomly select one objective marker and determine which unit has the most models within 3" of it (if the mission being played does not use objective markers, simply determine which unit has the most models within 3" of the centre of the battlefield). If more than one unit has the same number of models within 3" of the selected objective marker, randomly select one of these units. Roll one D6; on a 4+, that unit suffers D3 mortal wounds.
2	**Low on Ammunition:** *Orbital, aerial and overland supply routes alike have been severed, leaving warriors with nought but the ammunition supplies they carry with them. Even the weapons of the Tyranid aggressors are growing increasingly ineffectual, with the biomass of the world becoming ever more depleted. In such conditions, every shot must be made to count.* When resolving an attack with a ranged weapon, halve the maximum Range characteristic.
3	**Choking Spores:** *The atmosphere of this world is dense with clogging spores. Aircraft that linger too long find their engines choking and dying, sending them crashing to the ground.* At the start of the battle round, roll one D6 for each **AIRCRAFT** unit on the battlefield. On a 1, that unit suffers D3 mortal wounds.
4	**Rain of Death:** *As the world enters its terminal stage of being devoured, its tortured weather systems draw up vapours from the Tyranids' digestion pools and fling them back down in squalls of acidic bile. Organic and artificial matter alike breaks down beneath this devouring storm, sizzling steam rising from screaming victims as they writhe and melt away.* At the start of the battle round, the player going first rolls one D6; On a 5+, acidic rains begin to fall. Each **AIRCRAFT** unit and each other unit that is not wholly within a terrain feature suffers 1 mortal wound. At the start of each subsequent battle round, each **AIRCRAFT** unit and each other unit that is not wholly within a terrain feature suffers 1 mortal wound, and the player going first rolls one D6. On a 5+, the rain becomes a downpour; at the start of each subsequent battle round, each **AIRCRAFT** unit and each other unit that is not wholly within a terrain feature suffers D3 mortal wounds.
5	**Fighting Extinction:** *Driven before the devouring swarms, flushed from their disintegrating lairs by the biosphere's collapse, furious alpha-predators rampage wildly across the battlefield as they rage against their fate.* At the end of the battle round, the player who took the second turn selects one unit (friendly or enemy) that is on or within 3" of any terrain features and rolls one D6. On a roll of a 6, that unit suffers 1 mortal wound, or D3 mortal wounds if that unit contains 6 or more models. On a roll of 1-5, nothing happens and their opponent then repeats this process. Players alternate selecting units in this way until a 6 is rolled, or all eligible units have been selected. Each unit can be selected no more than once per battle round.
6	**The Devourer Cometh:** *To battle through the last days of a dying world is an experience no sentient being could endure without trauma. How long can warriors hold their nerve as the skies darken with bio-spores, the landscape breaks down into roiling, bubbling ruin and the colossal jaws of the Great Devourer close about them?* From the start of the third battle round onwards, when taking a Morale test for a unit, subtract 1 from that unit's Leadership characteristic. From the start of the fifth battle round, when taking a Morale test for a unit, subtract 2 from that unit's Leadership characteristic instead.

THEATRE OF WAR
DAEMON WORLD

Few battlefields in the 41st Millennium are as unnatural and terrifying as the surface of a Daemon world. Twisted out of true by warp-spawned sorcery and the whims of daemonic beings, worlds such as Sortiarius from *Psychic Awakening: Ritual of the Damned* can be evoked using these rules.

When fighting a battle on a Daemon world, the following rules apply:

SANITY-BLASTING LANDSCAPE

Daemon worlds are hellish landscapes that defy mortal comprehension. The sanity of even seasoned warriors can be pushed to breaking point.

In this battle, subtract 1 from the Leadership characteristic of every model (excluding **Chaos** and **Grey Knights** models) and add 1 to the Leadership characteristic of all **Daemon** models on the battlefield. In addition, in this battle the Insane Bravery Stratagem costs 3CP.

WARPED PERCEPTIONS

Here the natural laws of realspace have little purchase. Mortals would be wise not to take even the most fundamental facts of their reality for granted.

At the start of the battle round, each player rolls one D6. If the results are the same, then until the end of that battle round, each unmodified D6 result of a 1 counts as a 6 instead, and each unmodified D6 result of a 6 counts as a 1 instead.

THE MALEFIC REALM

Only the mad or foolish would willingly venture into the domain of the Daemons, for the denizens of the warp will swarm to mortal souls that invade their realm like moths to a flame.

In this battle, the Daemonic Incursion and Denizens of the Warp Stratagems (see *Codex: Chaos Daemons*) cost 1 fewer Command Points. In addition, any **Chaos Character** model that attempts a Daemonic Ritual (see *Codex: Chaos Daemons* or *Codex: Chaos Space Marines*) must roll one extra D6 when making the subsequent summoning roll.

BATTLEFIELD TWISTS

Before the battle, one player rolls one D6 and consults the battlefield twists table below, or both players can agree on the most suitable option. The result is an additional rule for the battle. This roll cannot be re-rolled, unless otherwise specified.

D6	BATTLEFIELD TWIST
1	**Warp Surge:** *The power of the warp flows strongly, lending great power to daemonic entities.* All **Daemon** models have a 4+ invulnerable save against attacks made with ranged weapons.
2	**Field of War:** *Mountains of skulls rise to the tortured skies, bubbling rivers of molten gore flowing between them. Through it all rolls the endless bellow of a wrathful war god, filling all who hear it with maddened might* Add 1 to the Strength characteristic of all models.
3	**Winds of Magic:** *The raw stuff of the warp howls across the battlefield in mutating gales. Those with the power and the nerve to do so can tap into this roiling source of empyric power, though not without great risk.* When a Psychic test is taken, add 2 to the result. In addition, unless the **Psyker** attempting to manifest the power is a **Daemon** or **Grey Knights** model, a Psychic test that includes any doubles will result in Perils of the Warp, not just a double 1 or 6.
4	**Fly Swarms:** *The very ground festers and rots, splitting open like a bloated corpse to disgorge roaring blizzards of fat-bodied Daemon flies.* When resolving an attack made with a ranged weapon against a target unit that is more than 18" away from your model, subtract 1 from the hit roll.
5	**Scent of Obsession:** *Where the haunting musk wafts from, none can say.* When an Advance or charge roll is made for a unit, add 1 to the result.
6	**World in Conflict:** *This battlefield is being contested by the Dark Gods, and the ground itself morphs and twists as their relative powers and influences wax and wane.* Roll twice more on this table (if you roll a double, or if either of the dice are a 6, roll both dice again until this is not the case). Apply both results.

TERRAIN TRAITS

Before the battle, one player should roll one D3 and consult the terrain traits table below, or both players can agree on the most suitable option. The result is an additional rule applied to all terrain features for the battle, other than Hills and **BUILDING** units. This roll cannot be re-rolled.

D3	TERRAIN TRAIT
1	**Cursed Ground:** *This place is steeped in the warp. It is a cursed place that is anathema to all science and reason.* When resolving an invulnerable saving throw for a model that is within 3" of this terrain feature, that saving throw is only successful on an unmodified roll of a 6. **DAEMON** models are unaffected by this trait.
2	**Aura of Mutation:** *A strange barrier surrounds this location, a shimmering field that can transform bullets into multi-coloured insects or turn las-bolts into drops of blood. However, this aura can also twist the flesh of those who shelter within it into something altogether more monstrous.* Models have a 4+ invulnerable save while they are within 3" of this terrain feature. Roll 2D6 at the end of your Movement phase for each unit from your army that is within 3" of this terrain feature. If the result is a double, that unit suffers a number of mortal wounds equal to the value on one of those dice (e.g. if you roll a double 4, that unit suffers 4 mortal wounds).
3	**Flux of Time:** *Time does not always flow linearly in the warp, speeding up or slowing down as befits the whim of the Chaos Gods.* At the start of the Fight phase, each player rolls one D6 for each unit from their army that is eligible to fight and is wholly within 3" of this terrain feature. On a 1-2, that unit cannot fight this phase until after all other eligible units have done so. On a 3-4, nothing happens. On a 5-6, that unit can fight first this phase.

MYSTERIOUS OBJECTIVE MARKERS

If you are using any objective markers, after determining deployment zones but before the first model is set up, one player should roll one D6 and consult the mysterious objective markers table below, or both players can agree on the most suitable option. The result is an additional rule applied to all objective markers for the battle. This roll cannot be re-rolled.

D6	MYSTERIOUS OBJECTIVE MARKER
1	**Possessed Objective:** *Daemons can be bound into places of power or dark significance, and they will take any opportunity to vent their anger at being so imprisoned.* At the start of the battle round, the players roll one D6 for each unit from their army that is within 3" of any objective markers. On a 1, that unit suffers D3 mortal wounds.
2	**Skull Altar:** *The skull of a dark champion lies here, its eye sockets constantly pouring forth blood. Any who gaze upon it are filled with a red-hot rage and the desire to kill, kill and kill again.* Add 1 to the Attacks characteristic of models while they are within 3" of any objective markers.
3	**Arcane Glyphs:** *An ever changing sigil is carved here, a symbol that flares bright in the presence of sorcery.* A **PSYKER** that is within 3" of any objective markers in the controlling player's Psychic phase can attempt to manifest one additional power that phase. Roll one D6 each time an enemy unit suffers a mortal wound in the Psychic phase whilst it is within 3" of any objective markers; on a 5+ that mortal wound is ignored.
4	**Aura of Entropy:** *An ill-omened quiet clots the air in this place like a long-inhabited sickroom; those who linger find their bodies withering with exhaustion and their wargear corroding into rusted, ineffectual ruin.* Reduce the Save characteristic of all models by 1 while they are within 3" of any objective markers (e.g. a Save characteristic of 5+ becomes 6+).
5	**Secrets from the Warp:** *Beguiling gems can be found here, and any who look within their facets hear a whispering voice in their mind, promising them knowledge beyond their dreams.* At the start of your Psychic phase, you can select one **CHARACTER** model from your army that is within 3" of any objective markers and roll 2D6; if the result is greater than that model's Leadership characteristic, that model's unit suffers 1 mortal wound – otherwise, you gain 1 Command Point.
6	**World in Flux:** *The realm of Daemons is ever in flux – mutable and fickle.* At the start of the battle round, the player who had the first turn rolls one D6 on this table; the result rolled takes effect until the end of that battle round (treat any further rolls of 6 as 1 instead).

THEATRE OF WAR
HIVE WORLD

Battling through the tangled confines and man-made mountains of a hive city presents combatants with countless challenges. Zemirus, depicted in *Psychic Awakening: Greater Good*, is but one example of such an artificial battlefield. Using these rules you can play out battles in your own tabletop hive cities, guiding your warriors through the manifold dangers and seizing advantage of the strategic boons that such an environment offers.

Designer's Note: *The rules for this Theatre of War can also be combined with those found in other city-fighting related supplements to create even more diverse battlefields (for example, the Cities of Death rules and Urban Battlezones in* Urban Conquest*).*

When fighting a battle on a hive world, the following rules apply:

HEIGHT ADVANTAGE

In urban warfare, every soldier in a tall building is a sniper, raking fire onto those below. Combating foes with such a height advantage is a dangerous proposition indeed.

A model gains a height advantage whilst it is occupying the upper levels of a Ruin or an Industrial Structure and it shoots at a unit that is either at street level or within a lower level of a Ruin or an Industrial Structure. To gain a height advantage, every model in the target unit must be on levels that are 3" or more below that of the firing model.

When resolving an attack made with a ranged weapon by a model, if that model has height advantage, improve the Armour Penetration characteristic of that weapon by 1 for that attack (e.g. AP 0 becomes AP -1, AP -1 becomes AP -2, and so on).

DARING LEAP

Battles are won or lost in the space of moments, with little enough time for laboriously moving soldiery up and down, floor after floor, of neighbouring hab-stacks or industrial shrines. Truly daring warriors will instead seize the moment, hurling themselves across the dizzying drop and spitting in the face of certain death.

In the Movement phase, when making a normal move with an **INFANTRY**, **BEAST** or **MONSTER** model that is on a terrain piece and not on the ground floor, you can measure directly to another point of equal or lower height when determining the distance moved, but when doing so you must halve that model's Move characteristic until the end of that phase. After doing so, roll one D6 for that model; on a 1, that model is destroyed.

BATTLEFIELD TWISTS

Before the battle, one player rolls one D3 and consults the battlefield twists table below, or both players can agree on the most suitable option. The result is an additional rule for the battle. This roll cannot be re-rolled.

D3	BATTLEFIELD TWIST
1	**Indiscriminate Ordnance:** *It is nigh impossible to accurately target long-ranged bombardments amidst the towering structures and stacked levels of a hive city. Sadly for combatants on the ground, this fact carries little weight with many generals.* After setting up terrain, divide the battlefield into six equal sections numbered 1-6. At the start of the battle round, roll one D6 to determine which section is hit by inaccurate shelling. Each player rolls one D6 for each unit from their army within that section. Subtract 1 from the result if the unit being rolled for is a **CHARACTER**. On a 5+, the unit being rolled for suffers D3 mortal wounds.
2	**Hostile Airspace:** *Amidst the tangle of flak batteries, auto-turrets and predatory snipers, aerial manoeuvre is severely limited.* Units that can **FLY** cannot make use of abilities that let them deploy in a location other than on the battlefield.
3	**Death at Every Turn:** *Cautiously do armies advance amidst the most tangled hivescape environs, only heavier armoured units daring to risk the inevitable hail of crossfire into which they must press.* Units that do not have the **VEHICLE** keyword cannot Advance in the first battle round.

MYSTERIOUS OBJECTIVE MARKERS

If you are using any objective markers, before determining deployment zones, one player should roll one D3 and consult the mysterious objective markers table below, or both players can agree on the most suitable option. The result is an additional rule applied to all objective markers for the battle. This roll cannot be re-rolled.

D3	MYSTERIOUS OBJECTIVE MARKER
1	**Hive-spirit Communion Uplink:** *Those who can tap into the machine spirits of a hive city's security monitoring network gain countless eyes with which to seek out and pinpoint their foes.* Whilst a model is within 3" of any objective markers, add 6" to the Range characteristic ranged weapons that model is equipped with.
2	**Sites of Sanctuary:** *Which side fortified this position, none living now remember. Regardless, the defences and prepared firing positions here will benefit your warriors now.* **INFANTRY**, **BEAST** and **SWARM** models within 3" of any objective markers receive the benefit of cover to their saving throw. In addition, when resolving an attack made by such a model, that model does not suffer the penalty for moving and firing Heavy weapons.
3	**Mobile Asset:** *Whether it be biddable data-servitors, grav-sleds loaded with precious artefacts or a stash of ammunition and fuel, hivescape battlefields often play host to strategic objectives that can be seized and relocated at will.* If the mission you are playing uses objective markers that can move, or can be moved, re-roll this result. In your Movement phase, when an **INFANTRY** unit within 3" of an objective marker that has no enemy models within 3" of it moves, after that unit has finished its move, if it did not Advance, you can move that objective marker so that it is in unit coherency with that unit. This cannot cause an objective marker to be removed from the battlefield, nor can it cause two objective markers to come within 6" of one another.

STRATAGEMS

If your army is Battle-forged, you have access to the Stratagems shown below whilst using this Theatre of War.

1CP — CAUGHT IN THE OPEN
Hive World Stratagem
In hive war, to eschew cover is to embrace death.

Use this Stratagem in your Shooting phase when a unit from your army is chosen to shoot with. Select one enemy unit that is wholly visible to the chosen unit and is not receiving the benefit of cover. Until the end of that phase, when resolving an attack made by a model in the chosen unit against the selected unit, if the target is within half range, you can re-roll the hit roll.

2CP — UNDERMINE
Hive World Stratagem
Sappers compromise the field from a lower level of the hive.

Use this Stratagem after determining deployment zones, but before the first unit is deployed. Select one terrain feature. Until the end of the battle, units do not gain the benefit of cover whilst they are within that terrain feature. In addition, unless it can **FLY**, when a unit makes any kind of move and any models in that unit would move within that terrain feature, subtract 2" from the maximum distance that all models in that unit can move.

THEATRE OF WAR
FORGE WORLD

Armies fighting on an operational forge world have the industrial might of their surroundings at their disposal, supplementing their war effort with supplies, repairs and data. Nonetheless, fighting in the thumping, grinding, automated heart of industrial macro machinery brings perils of its own. The rules found here allow you to set your battles in the Thalian Shoal, as featured in *Psychic Awakening: Engine War*, but can easily be used to represent rules for any forge world in your games of Warhammer 40,000.

When fighting a battle on the forge worlds of the Thalian Shoal, the following rules apply:

INDUSTRIAL HAZE
Concentrated industry has wreathed the battlefield in a haze of heat and smog, a perilous mix that reduces visibility and turns the atmosphere into a collection of noxious chemicals.

The maximum range of all ranged weapons is reduced to 30". Subtract 1 from Advance and charge rolls.

BATTLEFIELD TWISTS

Before the battle, one player rolls one D6 and consults the battlefield twists table below, or both players can agree on the most suitable option. The result is an additional rule for the battle. This roll cannot be re-rolled.

D6	BATTLEFIELD TWIST
1	**Data Uplink:** *The air here sings with rich noospheric data streams that can be tapped and employed for strategic gain.* Increase the range of aura abilities by 3". If your army is Battle-forged, roll one D6 each time you spend a Command Point on a Stratagem; on a 6, that Command Point is refunded.
2	**Rad Wastes:** *Leaking radiation from colossal reactor shrines has poisoned this region and rendered it inimical to life.* Unless it has the **Vehicle**, **Monster** or **Titanic** keyword, or has the **Adeptus Mechanicus** or **Chaos Daemon** Faction keyword, whilst a model is not within a terrain feature, subtract 1 from its Toughness characteristic.
3	**Promethium Repository:** *Refined promethium flows through pipes and conduits here, providing a rich, if volatile, strategic asset.* Add 3" to the Move characteristic of **Vehicle** models (if the model's Move characteristic has two values, add this to the maximum Move characteristic). When rolling to see if a **Vehicle** model explodes, crashes and burns or is subject to another, similar ability, add 1 to that roll.
4	**Auto-simulacra:** *Repair servitors thrum through the air, their programming compelling them to repair damaged machinery.* At the start of each player's turn, that player rolls one D6 for each **Vehicle** model in their army: on a 1, nothing happens; on a 2-3, that model regains 1 lost wound; on a 4-6, that model regains D3 lost wounds.
5	**Manufactorum Supplies:** *Ammunition crates are stacked to the skies here, providing a valuable resource for hard-pressed soldiery.* When a unit is chosen to shoot with, you can re-roll a single hit roll or wound roll.
6	**Thermic Industry:** *Vast forge shrines and furnaces fill the air with sweltering heat that swiftly exhausts combatants.* When resolving an attack made with a melee weapon, subtract 1 from the hit roll.

TERRAIN TRAITS

Designer's Note: *If playing using this Theatre of War, we recommend that the battlefield features plenty of industrial structure terrain features (Sector Mechanicus terrain features such as alchomite stacks, galvanic magnavents etc.). After setting up the battlefield, you should agree with your opponent which terrain features will be treated as Thalian forge world terrain features.*

Before the battle, one player should roll one D3 and consult the terrain traits table below, or both players can agree on the most suitable option. The result is an additional rule applied to all Thalian forge world terrain features other than **BUILDING** units. This roll cannot be re-rolled.

D3	TERRAIN TRAIT
1	**Smog Stacks:** *Smoke-blackened pipes belch clouds of obscuring fumes into the air.* Whilst a unit is within 1" of a Thalian forge world terrain feature, the maximum Range characteristic of all ranged weapons equipped on models in that unit is reduced to 12".
2	**Shield Generators:** *Strange energies shimmer from arcane machines, providing warriors with esoteric protection.* When resolving an attack made with a ranged weapon against a unit that is wholly within a Thalian forge world terrain feature, models in that unit gain a 5+ invulnerable save.
3	**Vociferous Machines:** *So furiously and noisily do the machines in this area toil that they disrupt and distract combatants.* Whilst a unit is within 1" of a Thalian forge world terrain feature, it cannot fire Overwatch and cannot be affected by the aura abilities of friendly models.

MYSTERIOUS OBJECTIVE MARKERS

If you are using any objective markers, after determining deployment zones but before the first model is set up, one player should roll one D6 for each objective marker; on a 4+, roll one D6 and apply the following result to that objective marker for the rest of the battle (these rolls cannot be re-rolled):

D6	MYSTERIOUS OBJECTIVE MARKER
1	**Volatile Tech:** *Strange energies flare and crackle perilously about this location.* At the end of the battle round, roll one D6. On a 1, all units within 3" of this objective marker suffer D3 mortal wounds.
2	**Skyfire Nexus:** *Powerful anti-aircraft ballistic cogitators aid your warriors in shooting down airborne foes.* Add 1 to hit rolls for attacks made with ranged weapons against targets that can **FLY** whilst the attacking model's unit is within 3" of this objective marker.
3	**Targeting Relay:** *The multi-spectral ballistic augurs found here aid and enhance your warriors' fire.* Re-roll hit rolls of 1 for attacks made with ranged weapons whilst the attacking model's unit is within 3" of this objective marker.
4	**Grav-wave Generator:** *Pulse generators throw out beating waves of gravitic energy that slow the approaching foe.* When making a charge roll for a unit, subtract 2 from that roll if any of the targets of its charge are within 3" of this objective marker.
5	**Scatterfield:** *Powerful holo-field generators throw up illusory fields to confound enemy targeting.* When resolving an attack made with a ranged weapon against a unit within 3" of this objective marker, subtract 1 from the hit roll.
6	**Power Conduit:** *A quick and dirty engine hack allows your warriors to tap into the lethal motive force that wells up here.* When resolving an attack made with a ranged weapon that has a random Damage characteristic (e.g. D3), when determining damage for that attack, add 1 to the roll if the attacking model's unit is within 3" of this objective marker (e.g. D3+1).

The Obsidian Jaguars' home world of Ceibhal depicted in *Psychic Awakening: Saga of the Beast* is typical of many such overgrown and deadly environs scattered across the Imperium. In such places the enemy are far from your only concern, for deadly flora and fauna prowl through the green-tinged gloom, seeking prey to devour. Using these rules you can transform your tabletop battlefield into a perilous jungle akin to those found not only on Ceibhal, but countless other worlds in the Imperium and beyond.

Designer's Note: *If playing using this Theatre of War, we recommend that the battlefield features plenty of Awakened Wyldwoods and Death World Forest terrain features. After setting up the battlefield, you should agree with your opponent which terrain features will be treated as areas of jungle terrain.*

When fighting a battle in a perilous jungle, the following rules apply:

SNAREVINES

These semi-sentient plants lie dormant upon the forest floor until they detect vibrations through the ground. When the source of those vibrations draws close the vines lash upwards, ensnaring limbs and weapons alike.

When a unit finishes an Advance or charge move within an area of jungle terrain, roll one D6 for that unit; on a 1, subtract 1 from hit rolls made for that unit until the end of the turn.

DEADLY PREDATORS

Even the clamour of battle is not enough to stop these apex predators from attacking warriors on the outskirts of the battlefield. Such beasts care nothing for the affiliations or intentions of those they hunt; they simply seek to sink fangs and claws into their next meal, and will attack with ferocious fury in order to do so.

At the start of the battle round, determine which unit on the battlefield is closest to a battlefield edge and roll one D6; on a 4+, that unit suffers D6 mortal wounds.

In addition, if both players agree, the following rules apply:

Infestation Units: Before the battle, the players must jointly gather at least four infestation units. These can be any units that have a Power Rating of 10 or less, but we recommend that players select units that do not share Faction keywords with any units from their own armies. In matched play games, infestation units can be any of the following units: **Beast** units, **Swarm** units, **Dreaded Ambull** units, **Genestealer** units, **Lictors**, **Spore Mines** or **Poxwalkers**. In open play and narrative play games, infestation units can be any unit, and players are encouraged to choose forces that best suit their own story, irrespective of their Power Rating. Perhaps a pack of Helbrutes is rampaging through the jungle, destroying all in their path, or an Officio Assassinorum Execution Force lurks in the trees ready to strike? Your choice is limited only by your miniatures collection.

Infestation units are treated as enemy units by both players. In the Fight phase, infestation units fight after all other units unless they have charged in their turn (see below). When resolving attacks or making saving throws etc. for infestation units, we recommend your opponent rolls the dice. The Command Re-roll Stratagem cannot be used to re-roll dice rolls made for infestation units.

Lurking in the Shadows: Before either side deploys, you must first infest the battlefield. To do so, you will need six objective markers: if there are fewer than six objective markers on the battlefield, the players must alternate setting up extra objective markers in areas of jungle terrain until there are six (these extra objective markers have no effect on any victory conditions). The players then randomly select three different objective markers, setting up a randomly selected infestation unit on each (all models in an infestation unit must be set up within 6" of their objective marker).

The Infestation Turn: At the end of the battle round, the infestation units have a 'turn'. In their Movement phase, each infestation unit will move as far as possible towards the closest objective marker (unless they are already within 3" of one), but they will not Fall Back or Advance. If they are a **Psyker**, they will attempt to manifest *Smite* in their Psychic phase (they will never attempt to Deny the Witch). In their Shooting phase, each model will shoot at the closest visible unit. If they are within 12" of any unit in their Charge phase they will attempt to charge the closest unit. In their Fight phase, each model will target the closest unit with all of its attacks. In all cases, infestation units will never target other infestation units, and if two units are equally close, randomly select which unit they will charge or target with their attacks. If any sequencing issues arise, the players roll off and the winner decides the order in which the rules in question are resolved.

BATTLEFIELD TWISTS

Before the battle, one player rolls one D3 and consults the battlefield twists table below, or both players can agree on the most suitable option. The result is an additional rule for the battle. This roll cannot be re-rolled.

D3	BATTLEFIELD TWIST
1	**Dense Flora:** *The foliage here is so thick that it is impossible to determine friend from foe, until they are almost close enough to touch – or to stab…* Units cannot be selected as the target of an attack made with a ranged weapon if they are more than 18" away from the firing model.
2	**Claustrophobic Environment:** *These hellish jungles are so dense that directing troops becomes a nightmare as orders are misinterpreted, entire units disappear from comms and even the air itself seems to stifle tactical thinking.* The maximum range of all aura abilities that affect friendly models is reduced to 1".
3	**Uncertain Footing:** *This area of jungle is a sodden mire, filled with bogs and areas of swampy ground. Heavily armoured warriors who take a wrong step disappear without a trace as the ground itself swallows them up.* At the end of your opponent's Movement phase you can select one **INFANTRY** model from your opponent's army that is not a **CHARACTER** and is within an area of jungle terrain and roll one D6, subtracting 1 from the result; if the result is greater than that model's Save characteristic, that model is destroyed.

MYSTERIOUS OBJECTIVE MARKERS

If you are using any objective markers, at the start of the first battle round but before the first turn begins, the player who is taking the first turn should roll one D3 and consult the mysterious objective markers table below, or both players can agree on the most suitable option. The result is an additional rule applied to all objective markers for the battle. This roll cannot be re-rolled.

D3	MYSTERIOUS OBJECTIVE MARKER
1	**Carnivorous Plants:** *The semi-sentient flora of this world are drawn towards the pulsing heat generated by blazing weaponry, powerful machines or collections of living bodies. They strike with sudden violence.* At the end of the battle round, roll one D6 for each unit that is within 3" of any objective markers; on a 1, that unit suffers 1 mortal wound.
2	**Ancient Stones:** *Command have indicated that your forces need to locate and control monoliths of an unknown material, deep in the jungle. However, these objectives emanate peculiar and contradictory energy fields, making them difficult to track and pinpoint until your forces are on top of them.* If the mission you are playing uses objective markers that can move, or can be moved, re-roll this result. At the start of the battle round, starting with the player who has the second turn, alternate selecting objective markers; for each objective marker, each player rolls a D6. The player who scores highest can move that objective marker up to 3" (they can be moved over models and terrain, but cannot leave the battlefield – if they would, reduce the distance they are moved by the minimum amount necessary). If the results are tied, that marker is not moved this battle round. The players should then repeat this process for each of the other objective markers until all objective markers have been selected.
3	**Hunting Supplies:** *Indigenous populations who dwell amidst the perils of infested and carnivorous jungles must rely upon both cunning and violence to endure. Many seed supply caches of hunters' arms through their territories, booby trapping them to ward off curious beasts and rival tribes.* Whilst a unit is within 3" of any objective markers, add 1 to the Leadership characteristic of models in that unit. If a unit finishes any type of move within 3" of an objective marker, roll one D6; on a 1 that unit suffers D3 mortal wounds.

DERELICT WORLD

Worlds scoured by war or disaster are not always seized by a new galactic power. Many are simply lost to the void, their structures rusting and their airwaves filled with slowly dying datagheists as the years crawl past. Bairsten Prime, depicted in *Psychic Awakening: War of the Spider*, is one example of such a world, and you can use the following rules to recreate it or to fashion your own derelict world battlefields.

Designer's Note: *If playing using this Theatre of War, we recommend that the battlefield features plenty of Sector Mechanicus terrain features (alchomite stacks, galvanic magnavents etc.) and ruins. After setting up the battlefield, you should agree with your opponent which terrain features will be treated as industrial terrain.*

When fighting a battle on the derelict world, the following rules apply:

VOX-NET INTERFERENCE

Whatever catastrophe claimed this world and its people, it also fouled the ionosphere for centuries to come.

Players cannot use the Command Re-roll Stratagem.

ENGINE THIRST

Little fuel remains for the engines of war upon this mournful and desiccated world.

Subtract 3" from the Move characteristic of models in **VEHICLE** and **BIKER** units, to a minimum of 0".

COMBATANT CONDITIONS

Before the battle, one player should roll one D3 and consult the combatant conditions table below, or both players can agree on the most suitable option. The result is an additional rule for the battle. This roll cannot be re-rolled.

D3	COMBATANT CONDITION
1	**War Weary:** *War upon derelict worlds involves great hardship. Soon even the hardiest of warriors will be physically exhausted.* Subtract 1 from the Strength characteristic of **INFANTRY**, **BIKER**, **CAVALRY**, **BEASTS** and **SWARM** models.
2	**Hollowed Out:** *The emptiness of a derelict world soon leeches into the souls of those who fight amidst its rusting ruins.* When taking a Morale test, roll one additional D6 and discard the lowest dice result. If both dice results are the same, select one of them to discard.
3	**To Walk Amidst the Ruin:** *Entropy has roughened this world's cracked surface until even open ground is treacherous to traverse.* When making a charge roll for an **INFANTRY**, **BIKER** or **CAVALRY** unit, roll one additional D6 and discard the highest dice result. If both dice results are the same, select one of them to discard.

BATTLEFIELD TWISTS

Before the battle, one player rolls one D3 and consults the battlefield twists table below, or both players can agree on the most suitable option. The result is an additional rule for the battle. This roll cannot be re-rolled.

D3	BATTLEFIELD TWIST
1	**Ghost Vox:** *Ghostly whispers and hollow wails for aid crackle amidst the static of broken vox channels.* When a player uses a Stratagem, but before the effects of that Stratagem are resolved, that player rolls one D6. On a 1, that Stratagem is not resolved, cannot be attempted again that phase, and the CPs spent are lost.
2	**Starved Guns:** *There is little ammunition to be scavenged upon a derelict world.* In your Shooting phase, after shooting with a unit, roll one D6. On a 1, models in that unit cannot make attacks with ranged weapons in both your and your opponent's next turns.
3	**The Dead Provide:** *Providence smiles upon those who stumble across the cached supplies of the long departed.* At the start of the battle round, roll one D6. If, at that point, the corresponding objective marker is controlled by a player, that player gains 1 Command Point.

ENVIRONMENTAL CONDITIONS

Before the battle, one player should roll one D3 and consult the environmental conditions table below, or both players can agree on the most suitable option. The result is an additional rule for the battle. This roll cannot be re-rolled.

D3	ENVIRONMENTAL CONDITION
1	**Fulminating Fury:** *Dry lightning lashes down from troubled skies, flagellating the cursed bedrock below.* At the start of each player's turn, they roll one D6 for each unit from their army that is on the uppermost floor of a Ruins terrain feature with multiple levels or is on the top level of an Industrial Structure terrain feature. On a roll of 1, that unit suffers D3 mortal wounds.
2	**Screaming Winds:** *Merciless gales tear at the dying land and churn the stagnant air to roiling fury.* In the Movement, Charge and Fight phases, models that can **FLY** and do not have the **AIRCRAFT** keyword cannot move over other models, and any vertical distance they move is counted towards the total they can move.
3	**Tectonic Instability:** *Ancient mining operations have left this world hollowed out and crumbling underfoot.* At the start of the battle round, the player who took the first turn rolls one D3; this roll cannot be re-rolled. On a 1, until the end of that battle round, halve the Move characteristic of models that cannot **FLY**.

STRATAGEMS

If your army is Battle-forged, you have access to the Stratagems shown below whilst using this Theatre of War.

2CP — DESERTION

Derelict World Stratagem

Morale erodes swiftly upon this mournful world.

Use this Stratagem at the start of the Morale phase. Select one enemy unit. At the end of that phase, for each model that fled that unit in that phase, one additional model flees.

1CP — CRUMBLING GRANDEUR

Derelict World Stratagem

All here is ruin. Even seemingly sturdy cover is not safe.

Use this Stratagem in your Shooting phase when an enemy model within 6" of a Ruins terrain feature is destroyed. Roll one D6; on a 2+, that model's unit suffers D3 mortal wounds.

THEATRE OF WAR
NECRON TOMB WORLD

To do battle upon an awakened tomb world such as Tredica Ardaxis in *Psychic Awakening: Pariah* is perilous indeed. These rules allow you to transform your battlefield into just such a deadly locale.

When fighting a battle on a Necron tomb world, the following rules apply:

FADE INTO THE DARK

The shadowy and disorienting interiors of tomb worlds are easy for warriors to get lost amidst, vanishing into the blackness never to return.

When a Morale test is failed, one additional model flees.

NULL-FIELD MATRIX

Tomb worlds are protected from psychic and daemonic manifestation by these merciless anti-empyric fields.

When a Psychic test is taken for a model, Perils of the Warp is suffered on any dice roll that is a double, instead of just a double 1 or a double 6. In addition, if a model suffers Perils of the Warp, do not roll any dice for the number of mortal wounds suffered; they suffer 3 mortal wounds instead.

BATTLEFIELD TWISTS

Before the battle, one player rolls one D3 and consults the battlefield twists table below, or both players can agree on the most suitable option. The result is an additional rule for the battle. This roll cannot be re-rolled.

D3	BATTLEFIELD TWIST
1	**Canoptek Wardens:** *Scuttling from the darkness come vicious Canoptek guard-constructs that set about unwary interlopers with mechanical savagery.* When a unit ends an Advance or charge move within 3" of any objective markers, roll one D6. On a 3+, the tomb world's defences activate and every unit within 3" of that objective marker suffers 1 mortal wound.
2	**Atomic Reconstitution Field:** *Nano-scarab repair beams pan this area, their emitters ill-equipped to distinguish friend from foe.* At the start of your turn, each **Vehicle** model in your army can regain up to 1 lost wound.
3	**Stilled Zone:** *Contra-empyric noctilith steles jut from walls and floor, deadening the energies of the warp.* When manifesting a psychic power, halve any distances mentioned in that psychic power.

MYSTERIOUS OBJECTIVE MARKERS

If you are fighting a battle that uses any objective markers, before deployment, one of the players should roll one D3 and consult the mysterious objective markers table below to see what additional rules apply to the objective markers on the battlefield. This roll cannot be re-rolled. This roll cannot be re-rolled.

D3	MYSTERIOUS OBJECTIVE MARKER
1	**Laid Bare:** *Parasitic power-siphons steal away even the most esoteric protective energies.* When resolving an attack made against a unit within 3" of any objective markers, an invulnerable saving throw cannot be made.
2	**Eldritch Energy Grid:** *Searing bolts of energy leap from one node to the next as some vast and ineffable machine awakens.* At the start of the battle round, roll one D6; on a 2+, the power network activates. If the power network activates, determine which objective markers are switched on by rolling two D6s. If two different objective markers are switched on, draw an imaginary straight line, 1mm wide, between them; each unit that this line passes across suffers D3 mortal wounds. If a double was rolled and only one objective marker is switched on, every unit within 6" of that objective marker suffers D3 mortal wounds instead.
3	**Improbability Field:** *These strange energy emanations scramble technological and empyric transit alike.* Enemy units that are set up on the battlefield as reinforcements cannot be set up within 9" of any objective markers.

TERRAIN TRAITS

Before the battle, one player should roll one D3 and consult the terrain traits table below, or both players can agree on the most suitable option. The result is an additional rule applied to the specified terrain features for the battle, other than **BUILDING** units. This roll cannot be re-rolled.

D3	TERRAIN TRAIT
1	**Noctilith Edifice:** *Formed from negatively energised blackstone, this site repels the energies of the warp even as it slowly, mercilessly leeches away the souls of those who fight in its shadow.* When a model would lose a wound as a result of a mortal wound in the Psychic phase while within 6" of a Ruins terrain feature, roll one D6; on a 4+ that wound is not lost.
2	**Scarab Replication Microfactory:** *This location plays host to energy wells that manufacture and spew forth chittering swarms of Canoptek Scarabs.* When the last remaining model in a **VEHICLE** unit is destroyed while within 6" of a Ruins terrain feature, roll one D6 before removing it from play. On a 2+, every other unit within 3" of that model suffers D3 mortal wounds.
3	**Counter-ballistic Interceptors:** *The defensive xenotech built into this region predictively plots hostile ballistic trajectories and discharge before employing localised rad-bursts to foul targeting systems and explode ordnance in mid-air.* At the start of your Shooting phase, until the end of that phase, subtract 6" from the Range characteristic of ranged weapons models are equipped with if their unit is within a Ruins terrain feature.

STRATAGEMS

If your army is Battle-forged, you have access to the Stratagems shown below whilst using this Theatre of War.

2CP

REANIMATION NODES
Tomb World Stratagem

The Master Program itself watches over this location with a portion of its machine intelligence, and is quick to bolster Necron self-repair systems where necessary.

Use this Stratagem at the start of the turn. Until the end of the turn, when making a Reanimation Protocols roll for a **NECRONS** model from your army whilst its unit is within 3" of any objective markers, re-roll a roll of 1.

1CP

TELEPORTATION GATES
Tomb World Stratagem

Shimmering green portals hang in the air, leading deeper into the labyrinthine tomb complex.

Use this Stratagem at the end of your Movement phase. Select one **INFANTRY** unit from your army wholly within 6" of any objective markers. Remove that unit from the battlefield and set it up anywhere on the battlefield wholly within 6" of an objective marker and more than 1" away from any enemy models.

The engine sanctum echoed with the hard clack of struck ordinator keys, the crackle and buzz of electrostatic charge and the monotonous screech of binharic plainsong. Glaring emerald light leapt and danced between its towering receptor shrines. Each exchange was accompanied by a deafening whip-crack of sound, a reek of ozone and a strobing burst of brilliance that transformed hunched tech-magi into statues wrought in green light and pitch darkness. The priests of Stygies VIII went about their labours with singular focus, appearing unperturbed by the harsh light and noise.

Lord Inquisitor Kyria Draxus watched them from the shadows of the outer atrium. Her breath misted slightly in the frigid air, each slow exhalation a tattered wisp, there and gone.

Dzaacho Mu-7 had sent for her. He had confirmed that the Xenarites had successfully extracted information from the data crystals she and her comrades recovered on Tredica Ardaxis. He had hinted at great revelations, yet had been typically miserly with the information he had recovered.

He wants to deliver it in person, she thought. He wants to revel in his own cleverness, cyborg detachment and emotionless logic be damned. On her shoulder, Shang gave a low croak and ruffled his leathery wings as a tinge of his mistress' impatience bled through their empathic bond. The Xenarites were crooked tools, as were so many of those she wielded in the Emperor's service.

As always, Lady Draxus calculated that the ends justified the means.

As always, she knew that her choices would be borne out.

As Draxus strode into the engine sanctum, Dzaacho Mu-7 withdrew his mechadendrites from a row of exload ports and shambled to meet her. Eight glittering optic lenses regarded the Lord Inquisitor from beneath a rubberised cowl. The leathery remnants of his flesh-mouth lolled and gasped out of time with his bellows breath, a forgotten organic remnant that troubled the Magos no more than would a fraying about the hem of his robes.

'Extension of welcome, Lord Inquisitor,' Dzaacho began, his voice a flat burr that emanated from vox-emitters somewhere beneath his robes.

'What have you learned?' she asked, cutting across whatever lengthy speech the Magos had prepared and causing his flesh-mouth to pucker sourly about its nutri-tubes.

'Information, Lord Inquisitor. Hard-won, sacred information. Advisory: the syntactic matrices at the core of the data are wholly xenos in meta-architecture. They could not be directly translated without exceeding operational–'

'The time you waste can be measured in Imperial lives, Dzaacho,' Draxus interrupted. 'What have you learned?'

The flesh-mouth puckered further, drool and unguent leaking from its corners, but none of the Magos' affront showed in his digitised voice.

'Explicatory: I mean only to explain in layman's terms why the data has been wrought into a visual artefact rather than a direct linguistic auto-transcript.'

'Show me then,' she said. 'What does the data tell us about the Pariah Nexus?'

'Revisory,' said the Magos as he turned towards a hulking ordinator and thrust his mechadendrites into its activation lectern. 'Pariah Nexus, plural form.'

'Plural…?' repeated Draxus, her voice trailing off as the ordinator's banks of overlapping screens flickered into wakefulness. She took in the hazy galaxy map wrought in green wire-frame lines. There, the bifurcating crimson smears of the Great Rift. There, signifier runes designating the positions of Holy Mars, Stygies VIII and other primary forge worlds. Yet her gaze was held by the xenoform glyphs that glowed poisonous green upon the screen. One here, in the Nephilim Sub-sector. Another, out beyond Vengeance upon the Eastern Fringe. Another far to the galactic north of Naogeddon. There were more, each incalculably distant from the next but undeniably forming a ring about the galaxy's fringe.

Or a noose, she thought with a chill.

'The glyph, what is its significance?' she asked, pleased to hear that her voice remained level and calm.

'Expository: it repeated a number of times throughout the information we were able to extract. Reiterative: direct translation was not possible, Lord Inquisitor, but the closest approximation we have been able to parse in High Gothic is…' His lenses flashed for a moment as he accessed the additional information. 'Szarekh, my Lord Inquisitor. The glyph signifies something called Szarekh.'

Kyria Draxus turned on her heel and marched from the chamber, leaving Dzaacho Mu-7 to call after her in bewilderment. His confusion and anger were less than nothing to her now. Nothing mattered but the data he had shown her.

'Emperor watch over your servants,' she breathed as she plunged back into the shadows. 'For it is so much worse than we feared.'